CONTENTS

Book 3.1

UNIT 2: NATURE LINKS

UNIT 3: BE CREATIVE!

UNIT 1: TELL ME MORE

UNIT 2: THINK IT THROUGH

UNIT 3: TURNING POINTS

Story Elements

The **setting** is where and when a story takes place. The **characters** are the people the story is about.

Read the story. Then answer each question.

> My name is Dawn. I live on a farm in New Jersey. Our farm has hills with apple trees. Every fall, the apples on our trees are ready to be picked.
>
> Every fall, Grandmother María comes from Texas to visit us. Together, we make apple juice and apple pies. She tells me stories. My favorite stories are about my father when he was a boy.
>
> "When your father was the same age as you, he rode horses," Grandmother María said.
>
> "Where did he ride?" I asked.
>
> "All over our ranch," Grandmother María said.
>
> Then she told me that Texas was so big that a boy could ride all day and never see a house or a person. She said that instead of apple trees, my father saw cactus plants.

1. Where does Dawn live? <u>**on a farm where apple trees grow**</u>

2. Where is the farm? <u>**in New Jersey**</u>

3. When does Dawn pick apples? <u>**in the fall**</u>

4. Who are the three characters in the story? <u>**Dawn, Grandmother María, Dawn's father**</u>

5. Who is Grandmother María's story about? <u>**Dawn's father when he was a boy**</u>

6. Where is Grandmother María's story set? <u>**on a ranch in Texas**</u>

McGraw-Hill School Division

At Home: Have students make up a <u>story</u> about someone <u>visiting</u> them. Have them identify their story's characters and settings.

Vocabulary

Supply the correct words from the list.

scattered   enormous   towering   journey   surrounded   astonished

The long ___journey___ to the center of the desert was well worth it.

Everything we saw there ___astonished___ us. It was all so different!

Wonders of nature ___surrounded___ our campsite in every direction. There

were ___enormous___ sand drifts that seemed to sweep across the desert

floor like huge tidal waves. Overhead were ___towering___ cliffs made of red

and black sandstone.

The most amazing thing we saw was the tumbleweed ___scattered___

about the desert for miles and miles. Strong, warm winds whipped them

into action. We marveled as they danced across the horizon.

At Home: Have students read the dictionary definitions
for each of the vocabulary words.

The Dream

I always remember my dreams. Usually they are about a *journey*. In last night's dream my journey was very strange. It *astonished* and amazed me.

In my dream, my bed was as *enormous* as a swimming pool. While I was in it, it rolled out of the house and onto the sidewalk. On the sidewalk there were many toys *scattered* under tall, *towering* trees.

I stopped my huge bed from rolling by grabbing one of the trees. Then I climbed down a giant ladder to get off my bed. On the ground, I was *surrounded* by the greatest toys I had ever seen in my life. What a dream!

1. How did the author feel about the dream?

   astonished, amazed

2. What types of dreams does the author best remember?

   dreams about a journey

3. What things are *scattered* in the dream?

   toys

4. What two words describe the size of things in this dream?

   towering, enormous

5. Why might the dreamer have been happy the bed rolled outside?

   There were great toys outside to play with.

At Home: Have students draw a picture of two things at home that are enormous.

2A

Story Comprehension

Read each statement. Write **T** if the statement describes "Grandfather's Journey." Write **F** if the statement does not correctly describe "Grandfather's Journey."

1. __F__ The grandfather first left Japan when he was an old man.

2. __T__ Grandfather traveled to North America on his journey.

3. __T__ Grandfather saw the desert on his trip to the New World.

4. __F__ The grandfather explored North America by covered wagon.

5. __T__ For part of his journey, Grandfather traveled by steamship.

6. __F__ The grandfather liked Florida best.

7. __T__ Grandfather returned to Japan to get married and because he was homesick.

8. __T__ The grandson went to California because his grandfather had told him stories about the place.

9. __T__ The grandfather, his new wife, and baby daughter lived in San Francisco.

10. __F__ The grandson now lives in China.

At Home: Have students imagine a faraway place that they would like to visit. Have them write down reasons why they would like to go and things they would expect to find there.

Use Book Parts

The **author** and the **title** of a book appear on both the front cover and the side of the book, or **spine**.

Old Friends Joe Parker	**Cooking with Woks** Li Woo
Victorian Porches Selma Davidson	*Kindergarten Art* Harry Waters
Painting Easter Eggs Paula Brunst	**JUMP ROPE** Rhonda Newcomb
COMPUTER REPAIR Kathy Verang	Bonsai Trees Larry Larsen
Wigs and Hats Rhonda Newcomb	**Scary Stories** Paula Arnot

Use the stacks of books to answer these questions.

1. Who wrote a book about art in kindergarten? <u>Harry Waters</u>

2. What is the title of the book written by Joe Parker? <u>Old Friends</u>

3. If your computer was broken, which book would you need? <u>Computer Repair</u>

4. Who wrote more than one book in these piles? <u>Rhonda Newcomb</u>

5. What is the title of the book about cooking? <u>Cooking with Woks</u>

6. Who wrote Scary Stories? <u>Paula Arnot</u>

7. What is the name of the book that Larry Larsen wrote? <u>Bonsai Trees</u>

8. Which book did Paula Brunst write? <u>Painting Easter Eggs</u>

At Home: Ask students which book they would look in to find information about miniature trees.

Story Elements

Grandfather is the main **character** in "Grandfather's Journey." Japan and North America are the **settings**, or places where the story happens. Answer the questions about the main character and settings in the chart below.

CHARACTER:	SETTINGS:
Grandfather	**North America**
1. Why does Grandfather leave Japan? <u>to see the world</u>	4. What does Grandfather like best about California? <u>sun, seacoast, mountains</u>
	Japan
2. What does Grandfather like best when he returns to Japan? <u>seeing old friends, seeing mountains and rivers</u>	5. Why does Grandfather decide not to build a house in his village? <u>He thinks a city is a better place for his daughter to grow up.</u>
3. What does Grandfather tell his grandson stories about? Why? <u>California; he misses it even though he is happy at home in Japan.</u>	6. Why does Grandfather spend the end of his life in his village? <u>War destroyed his home in the city.</u>

McGraw-Hill School Division

5

At Home: Have students make a drawing for one story setting. Write a sentence that describes the drawing.

Book 3.1/Unit 1
Grandfather's Journey

6

Make Predictions

You can use what you have learned about a character in a story to **predict** what this character might do. Read each story. Then answer the questions.

Tanisha is good at solving problems. She also likes taking care of her little brother. Last summer, Tanisha and her family went on a camping trip. One afternoon, Tanisha and her little brother got lost on the way from their tent to the car. Tanisha's brother became scared and started to cry.

1. Will the children find their way back to the tent? How do you know?

    Yes; Tanisha is good at solving problems.

Tonight, Jerry has to finish a science project for school. Tomorrow is the science fair. They are giving prizes for the best project. Jerry would really like to win a prize. Tonight, Jerry's favorite TV show is on from eight o'clock to eight-thirty. Jerry has to go to bed at eight-thirty.

2. Will Jerry finish his science project? Why?   **Yes; he wants to**

    win a prize.

3. When will Jerry work on his science project? **before his TV show**

Wendy lives in the country. The ocean is far away. Her favorite books are about boats. She dreams of sailing far and fast across the ocean.
    Last summer, Wendy's father asked her to choose what they would do on their next summer trip.

4. What will Wendy and her father do on their next summer trip?

    They will go sailing.

McGraw-Hill School Division

4 Book 3.1/Unit 1
Grandfather's Journey

At Home: Have students pick a character from a movie. Ask students to describe what the character is like and predict something that the character might do.

Compound Words

A **compound word** is a word that is made up of two smaller words. Each word in a compound word can stand alone.

brake + man = brakeman

Use the picture clues to write the compound word. The first part of the compound word appears below.

		First Word	**Compound Word**
1.		basket	<u>**basketball**</u>
2.		rail	<u>**railroad**</u>
3.		home	<u>**homework**</u>
4.		camp	<u>**campground or campfire**</u>
5.		jelly	<u>**jellyfish**</u>

At Home: Ask students to tell you three more examples of compound words.

McGraw-Hill School Division

Problem and Solution

The answer you find to a **problem** is called the **solution**.

Draw a line between the problem and its matching solution.

Problem   **Solution**

1. There is a lot of snow on the ground.

   a. My mother will bring the bike to a bike shop.

2. My baby sister was crying.

   b. My dad bought a big umbrella for us to sit under.

3. My bike has a flat tire.

   c. I wear my boots to school.

4. Our babysitter is on a trip, and my parents are going out on Friday night.

   d. Mom helps me get dressed in the morning.

5. My dad has no time to paint the house.

   e. We replaced the glass.

6. We can't sit in our backyard because it's too hot.

   f. I rocked the baby to sleep.

7. I broke my arm, and I can't button my shirt.

   g. My grandparents offer to spend the weekend.

8. My brother broke a window.

   h. He hires a painter.

8 Book 3.1/Unit 1
Phoebe and the Spelling Bee

At Home: Have students write another problem and solution pair.

8

Vocabulary

Write a vocabulary word from the list that means almost the same thing as the underlined words.

legend   correct   groaning   unusual   continue   embarrass

1. Do you think an octopus is a strange and ____**unusual**____ animal?

2. We were <u>right</u>, she gave us the ____**correct**____ answer.

3. Spilling milk in front of twenty people might <u>shame</u> or ____**embarrass**____ you.

4. A ____**legend**____ and a <u>folk tale</u> are similar kinds of stories.

5. The bear held its injured paw and started <u>moaning</u> and ____**groaning**____ in pain.

6. <u>Keep going</u>, ____**continue**____ to the next green light.

At Home: Have students create a crossword puzzle using the vocabulary words.

Book 3.1/Unit 1
Phoebe and the Spelling Bee
6

McGraw-Hill School Division

Eric and the Happy Answer

Once there was a boy named Eric. Eric liked to be *correct*. If his teacher said he was doing something the wrong way, Eric would still *continue*. "I would *embarrass* myself if I said I had been wrong," he thought.

One day Eric's teacher heard him *groaning* at his desk. "Why are you making such an *unusual* sound?" she asked. "You sound like a strange creature in a *legend* or tall tale."

"I don't want to think I'm always right," Eric said. "Next time I'm doing something wrong will you help me do it right?"

"Of course!" the teacher replied.

From that day on, things changed for Eric.

1. Who always thought he had to be *correct*?

   Eric

2. What was Eric afraid he would do if he said he was wrong?

   embarrass himself

3. What *unusual* thing did his teacher hear Eric doing?

   groaning

4. What did Eric sound like when he was *groaning*?

   a creature in a legend

5. Why did things change for Eric?

   He decided he would ask his teacher for help.

McGraw-Hill School Division

At Home: Have students write about a time they asked for help. Were they afraid to ask? Were they happy they did?

Story Comprehension

Answer the questions about "Phoebe and the Spelling Bee."

1. Why is Phoebe afraid of Friday? __Phoebe is afraid because__

   __Mrs. Ravioli has planned a spelling bee.__

   _____

2. Why does Phoebe pretend to be sick at school? __She hasn't studied__

   __her spelling words.__

   _____

3. How is Katie different from her friend Phoebe? __Katie likes spelling,__

   __and she is not afraid of the spelling bee.__

   _____

4. How does Phoebe upset Katie? __Phoebe lied to her and the class.__

   _____

   _____

5. How does Phoebe make up for what she does to Katie? __She gives__

   __Katie a tulip and studies hard for the spelling bee.__

   _____

6. Why do Phoebe and Katie get certificates? __Katie gets her certificate__

   __for good spelling. Phoebe gets hers for good imagination.__

   _____

McGraw-Hill School Division

Use a Glossary

A **glossary** is a list of words and definitions for a specific book.

<u>124   Shetland pony–Stomp</u>

Shetland pony (noun)   1. a small-built pony of a breed that came from the
    Shetland Islands
shortchange (verb)   1. to give less money back than is owed   2. to cheat or trick
shoe (noun)   1. a covering for the foot   2. a piece of metal for a horse's foot
slouch (verb)   1. to sit with an awkward, drooping posture
snake oil (noun)   1. a worthless preparation sold as medicine
sofa bed (noun)   1. a couch that unfolds into a bed
son (noun)   1. a male child
springer spaniel (noun)   1. a dog having drooping ears and a silky brown and
    white coat
stomachache (noun)   1. a pain in the belly

Use the part of a glossary page above to answer these questions.

1. Is *stomachache* a noun, verb, adverb, or adjective? ____<u>noun</u>____

2. What word comes after *shoe* in this glossary? _____<u>slouch</u>_____

3. To find the definition of the word *stories*, would you look before or after

   this page in the glossary? Explain. <u>after — "story" comes after</u>

   <u>"stomp" (the second guide word for this page) in alphabetical order.</u>

4. What are the guide words for the page on which *son* appears?

   <u>Shetland pony, stomp_____</u>

5. Pretend you saw the word *shoe* in a story about an animal who can't

   walk because of sore feet. Which of the two definitions shown in the

   glossary would apply? Write that definition. <u>2. a piece of metal</u>

   <u>for a horse's foot_____</u>

5 Book 3.1/Unit 1
Phoebe and the Spelling Bee

At Home: Ask students to think of another word that
would fall between the guide words on this glossary
page.

11

Problem and Solution

One subject in school presents **problems** for the main character in "Phoebe and the Spelling Bee." Read each problem in the chart below. Then write the solution Phoebe finds for the problem.

Problem

1. Phoebe needs to learn how to spell **actor** correctly.

2. On Tuesday, Mrs. Ravioli asks Phoebe if she's looked at the spelling list yet. Phoebe has not spent a lot of time on spelling.

3. Mrs. Ravioli gives a practice spelling bee, and Phoebe is not ready for it.

4. Katie is mad at Phoebe for lying to her.

5. Phoebe wants to learn how to spell the word **method**.

6. Phoebe misspells the word **brontosaurus**.

Solution

1. She thinks of the word act and or in a sentence.

2. Phoebe shares a sentence with the class that shows that she has at least read the words.

3. Phoebe pretends she is sick and goes to the nurse's office.

4. Phoebe brings Katie a tulip and says she is sorry.

5. She makes up a story about a caveman whose name is Me, Thod.

6. She shares her spelling stories with the class, and everyone enjoys them.

At Home: Have students use Pheobe's spelling techniques. Have them write stories to help them remember this week's spelling words.

12

Book 3.1/Unit 1
Phoebe and the Spelling Bee
6

Make Predictions

What you learn in a story can help you **predict** what will happen next. Read each story. Then answer the questions.

> Mrs. Miller is ninety years old. She lives alone in a small house. Three children live next door to Mrs. Miller. Every Saturday they visit her. Sometimes they help her do things around the house. Lately, Mrs. Miller has been feeling a little tired. She has not been able to rake the leaves or weed her garden.

1. What might happen the next time the children visit Mrs. Miller?

   They will help her take care of her yard.

2. What parts of the story helped you make your prediction? **The children live next door; they visit Mrs. Miller; they help her do things around the house.**

> Elaine and Michael found soda cans all over the sidewalk. They thought the cans made the street look messy. So they began collecting the cans. Elaine's father told the children about a new store down the block that bought soda cans for a nickel each.

3. What do you think might happen next in the story? **Elaine and Michael will take the cans they collected, bring them to the store, and earn money.**

4. What parts of the story helped you make your prediction? **The children were collecting the cans. A store down the street buys soda cans.**

At Home: The next time students begin a TV program or a book, ask them to predict an outcome. Have them write down their prediction, and then check it when they find out the outcome.

13

Prefixes

A **prefix** is a word part that can be added to the beginning of a word. It creates a new word with its own meaning. The prefix **un-** means "not," or "opposite of." For example, the word **unfair** means "not fair" or "the opposite of fair."

Below each sentence, write the word that includes the prefix **un-**. Then write the meaning of the word.

1. It was unlucky that Mona was sick on the first day of vacation.

   unlucky—not lucky

2. The story has an unusual character named Simon.

   unusual—not usual, different

3. The movie was very interesting, even though it was untrue.

   untrue—not true, false

4. It took the child a long time to unwrap her birthday present.

   unwrap—take off wrapping

5. The number of stars in the sky is unknown.

   unknown—not known

6. Jack was unhappy that he did not get a better score in the game.

   unhappy—not happy

At Home: Ask students to name three other words that begin with the prefix **un-**.

Steps in a Process

A series of steps you follow in order are called **steps in a process**.

The steps below in each set are not in order. Write numbers 1 through 4 on the lines to show the order.

Shop for Spaghetti

__3__   Put noodles in shopping cart.

__1__   Go to the store.

__2__   Choose a shopping cart.

__4__   Pay for the noodles.

Go Skating with a Friend

__4__   Skate down the street together.

__1__   Find skates in closet.

__2__   Put on right and left skates.

__3__   Skate to friend's house.

Cook Spaghetti

__4__   Put the cooked noodles on a plate.

__1__   Go to the kitchen.

__2__   Open the box of noodles.

__3__   Cook the noodles in a pan.

Go to School

__4__   Walk out the door.

__3__   Pick up the school books.

__1__   Wake up on time.

__2__   Get dressed.

At Home: Help students to identify a step-by-step process that they follow at home. Have them write down the steps in order.

Vocabulary

Supply the correct words from the list:

length   guard   royal   within   gift   straighten

Once a prince and a princess lived happily in an underground castle. There was one problem, though. The _____**royal**_____ kingdom always looked boring and dull. So the prince had an idea. As a birthday _____**gift**_____ he bought the princess some paintings to decorate the castle walls.

The princess was thrilled! Her favorite painting showed a small face tucked _____**within**_____ a larger face. She hung this one on the castle door, next to the _____**guard**_____ who protected them. Another painting showed a group of bent and slanted lines. If you looked at the lines long enough, they seemed to _____**straighten**_____ out. Looking at this will keep people busy, she thought.

After three days all of the paintings were hung, except one. This last painting is shown below. Do you think the lines are the same _____**length**_____ ?

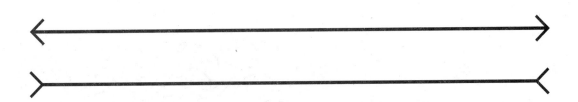

Anything Can Happen!

I used to visit the land of make-believe very often. *Within* the land of make-believe, anything can happen! Once, an old woman offered me a ring as a *gift*. The ring changed shape as fast as I could say "one, two, three." Then I made it *straighten* out into a long magic wand.

With my magic wand I knew I could become anyone and anything I wished. I decided to become a *guard* for a *royal* family. I marched up and down the *length* of their long hallway. Then I marched right into the royal kitchen. You can find all kinds of cookies and cakes in the land of make-believe!

1. What kind of family lived in the castle?

   royal

2. What did the speaker have to do to change the ring to a wand?

   straighten it

3. What kind of person watches over *royal* families?

   a guard

4. When you measure from one end to the other of the castle hall, what do you learn?

   its length

5. What is special about the land of make-believe?

   Anything can happen there.

At Home: Encourage students to write about what they would like to find within the world of make-believe.

16A

Story Comprehension

Review the optical illusions shown in "Opt." Then list two of the illusions under each heading. **Answers may vary. Sample answers are shown.**

What Colors Do You See?	**How Many Objects?**
1. White balloon appears green.	3. Trident prongs change in number.
2. Gray dots appear where white lines cross.	4. Six blocks become seven.
The Same Size?	**Hidden Faces?**
5. Red tape appears longer than blue.	7. Faces are hidden in portraits.
6. King appears taller than queen.	8. Faces are hidden in zoo animals.
Straight or Crooked?	**Changing Shapes?**
9. Vertical lines on cloak appear crooked.	11. Kites appear flat or box-shaped.
10. Fishing rod appears crooked.	12. The dragon's eyes seem to spin.

Use a Table of Contents

Use the headings below to fill in two tables of contents. Notice that one table of contents is for a book of fiction, that is, a made-up story. The other is for a nonfiction book, which is about real things.

Nailing the Box Together 17   Meteorite Science Project 12

by Claire Rollins   Snacks From Saturn 31

Clearing the Ground 2   Harvesting Your Crop 53

Grade School on Mars
by Claire Rollins
Riding The Rocket Bus. 3
Airlock Homeroom 8
Meteorite Science Project. 12
Alien Visitors. 15
Weightless Gym Class 19
Adventures in the Cafeteria. 23
Food in a Tube 27
Snacks From Saturn. 31
Sandboxes in the Craters 37
After School Moon Walk 42

Building A Winter Garden
by Gina Lawrence
Clearing the Ground 2
Building a Frame 7
Cutting the Wood 13
Nailing the Box Together 17
Attaching a Glass Top 28
Planting Lettuce 34
Keep The Ground From Freezing . .41
Harvesting Your Crop 53
Replanting For Summer 67
Terrarium Gardens, Too 78

At Home: Ask students to identify which of the above tables of contents is for a nonfiction book and which is for a fictional story.

Steps in a Process

Think about the steps you use when you solve a problem. Often you can use the same steps to solve other problems. Writing down the steps will help you remember them. A series of steps you follow in order are called **steps in a process**.

Read Problem 1 and the list of steps for solving it below. Then write a list of steps for solving Problem 2.

Problem 1

What steps will help you find out if the vertical lines of the messenger's cloak are crooked or straight?

Process

1. Measure the distance between two lines near the top.
2. Write down that number.
3. Measure the distance between the same two lines near the bottom.
4. Write down this number.
5. Compare your two measurements. If they are the same, the lines are straight.

Problem 2

In the picture of the Royal Pet at the zoo, what steps will help you decide if the body of the pet is shorter than its neck?

Process

1. **Measure the length of the neck.**

2. **Write down that number.**

3. **Measure the length of the body.**

4. **Write down this number.**

5. **Compare the two measurements. If the second number is less, the body is shorter.**

At Home: Have students follow the steps they wrote. What did they discover about the length of the Royal Pet's neck and body? Have them record the results.

19

Book 3.1/Unit 1
Opt: An Illusionary Tale

5

Story Elements

The **narrator** tells the story. Often, the narrator is one of the **characters**, or people in the story. The narrator tells the story from his or her own **point of view.**

Read each part of the story below. Then answer the questions about it.

> The queen called me. I was on the other side of the room. "Princess Lulu," the queen said. "How long will it take you to get from there to here?"

1. Who are the two main characters? <u>**Princess Lulu and the queen**</u>

2. What two words tell you that Princess Lulu is the narrator? <u>**I, me**</u>

> My brother, Randy, told me a funny story. I have never laughed so hard in all my life! My brother is such a clown! He says he's glad I am his sister.

3. Who are the main characters? <u>**Randy's sister, Randy**</u>

4. Who is the narrator? What words help you to know this? <u>**Randy's**</u> <u>**sister; she talks about herself using the words "my," and "I."**</u>

> The dog's name is Toaster. The brown spots on his white fur are shaped like pieces of toast. Ernie is Toaster's owner. Ernie named his dog Toaster.

5. Who are the two main characters? <u>**Toaster and Ernie**</u>

6. Is the narrator one of the two main characters? How do you know?

<u>**No; if either of these characters was the narrator, the story would**</u>

<u>**be told from his point-of-view**</u>

At Home: Have students narrate a story. Then have them try to tell their stories from a different point of view.

Prefixes

You can add the **prefixes un-** or **dis-** to the beginnings of some words to make new words. The prefix **un-** means "opposite of" or "not." The prefix **dis-** also means "opposite of" or "not."

Rewrite each sentence. Replace the underlined phrase with a word from the box that includes the prefix **un-** or **dis-**. Look at the following example:

Sean was <u>not lucky</u> flying the kite.

Sean was **un**lucky flying the kite.

unusual	unknown	displeased	disobeyed	unbelievable

1. The stranger was <u>not known</u> to the family.

   The stranger was unknown to the family.

2. Jeri <u>did not please</u> her science teacher.

   Jeri displeased her science teacher.

3. Quong's painting was <u>not the same as everyone else's.</u>

   Quong's painting was unusual.

4. My little brother can yell so loud it is <u>not believable.</u>

   My brother can yell so loud it is unbelievable.

5. Bruce <u>did not obey</u> the rule.

   Bruce disobeyed the rule.

Problem and Solution

Characters in stories often face **problems**. The answers to their problems are called **solutions**. Read the problems below. Then complete the chart by writing down two ways to solve each problem. **Answers will vary.**

Problem	**Solutions** Answers will vary.
Your class is going to write letters to pen pals. Everyone's pencil point is broken and there is no sharpener. What can the class do?	1. Use pen or crayons to write your letters. 2. Buy a new pencil sharpener.
A vacant lot across the street from your school is covered with rocks. Nobody likes looking at the lot. What can your school do?	3. Make a rock garden out of the rocks. 4. Clear the rocks and plant a garden.
It is your friend's birthday. You forgot to buy a present. What can you do?	5. Give your friend one of your favorite things. 6. Promise your friend that you'll buy a present tomorrow.

6 Book 3.1/Unit 1
Max Malone

At Home: Help students to identify problems in their neighborhoods. Brainstorm together to find some solutions.

22

Vocabulary

Supply the correct words from the list.

scene   ceiling   eager   including   section   cents

Juliana was _____**eager**_____ to see the new house.

She couldn't wait! There was even a picture of a carnival

painted in her new bedroom. "It's on the _____**ceiling**_____,"

her father had said. "You'll be able to see it as you lie in bed."

Juliana thought a carnival was a great _____**scene**_____ to

watch before falling asleep.

There was another thing that Juliana liked about her new

house. Even _____**including**_____ a ten-minute bus ride, the

house was still closer to school.

Juliana's mother bought her a new book bag for the daily trip.

It was a present to celebrate their moving. The bag cost seven

dollars and eighty _____**cents**_____. They found it in the

sports _____**section**_____ of the department store.

"Of all places!" Juliana's mother exclaimed as she picked up

the bag. "You never know where you'll find things!"

At Home: Have students use each vocabulary word in a sentence.   Book 3.1/Unit 1
Max Malone   6

Tanya's Books

Tanya ran out of books to read. So one day she decided to write her own book. She was *eager* to start. "It will have neat stuff, *including* pictures," she said.

Tanya's mother gave Tanya ninety *cents* to buy a new pen. Then Tanya began to write. Her story was about a house where the *ceiling* became the floor. In one *scene*, the family in the house tried to eat breakfast upside down.

The story was so funny, Tanya decided to write a longer story. This second story had five sections. Each *section* told about a friend of hers.

When Tanya finished her second story she gave each of her friends a copy. Everyone liked it.

1. What did Tanya do when she ran out of books to read?

   She started writing her own stories.

2. What does the floor become in Tanya's first book?

   the ceiling

3. What word tells how Tanya feels about writing her books?

   eager

4. What word describes one setting and event in Tanya's first book?

   scene

5. How much money did Tanya's mother give her?

   ninety cents

At Home: Encourage students to talk about what kind of story they would write if they ran out of books to read.

Story Comprehension

Look back over "Max Malone." Then complete the chart below.
Answers may vary.

1. Setting of story	Toys for Less, outside and inside the sporting-goods store, Austin's house
2. Main characters	Max, Gordy, Austin
3. Beginning of story	Max and Gordy figure out a way to make money by selling baseballs.
4. Middle of story	Max and Gordy sell all their baseballs to people who want Dusty Field's autograph. They also get autographs from Dusty Field for themselves and their sick friend, Austin.
5. End of Story	Max and Gordy visit Austin and give him a baseball autographed by Dusty Field.

Now match each detail.

6. __c__ sells all the baseballs for $5   **a.** Dusty Field

7. __e__ had his appendix taken out   **b.** Max

8. __a__ a baseball player   **c.** Toys are Less

9. __b__ gets idea to buy baseballs for $5   **d.** Gordy

10. __d__ helps Max sell the baseballs   **e.** Austin

Use an Index

An **index** can help you find information in a nonfiction book.
The numbers for pages with illustrations are set in italics.

---

622 – **Index**

M
magazines, financial 33, *34*
merit system, 101, 532
merchant class, 36, *88*
   rise of in England, 385, *412*
money systems, 65, 89–101
mutual funds, 56, 92
   failure of, 109–120

N
Native American money, 34
newspaper, listings of exchange rates,
   56–58
numbers, 35
   early mathematics 59

numismatics, 67–73
   coin collecting, 122

O
Old World, 45
   gold in, 310
   money used in, 99, 134, 238, 259–261
oversupply, 145, 267

P
Pacific Island coins, 67, 90
   rise of the dollar, 578, 655–678
   shells, 202, 349
   trading, 381, 399, *412*, *424*
pound, English, 78–80

---

1. On what page would you find information on Native American money?

   34

2. Where would facts about money systems be found?

   pages 65, 89-101

3. Besides page 202, where else would you read about shells being used
   as Pacific Island money? _____349_____

4. If you wanted to know how paper money is printed in the United States,
   would this page of the index help you to find out? _____**no**_____

5. Which page probably has an illustration of a financial magazine? __34__

6. On which pages would you find information about the failure of mutual
   funds? ____109–120____

Problem and Solution

You can often find **solutions,** or answers, to even the most difficult **problems.** Finish the chart by writing down how Max and Gordy solved each of their problems.

Problem	**Solution**
1. Max and Gordy have $2.50 each and want to buy as many 20¢ baseballs as they can.	They talk to a store manager who sells them all the balls for $5.00.
2. Max and Gordy feel shy about selling their baseballs to people at the sporting-goods store.	They force themselves to call out to people to buy their baseballs for Dusty Field's autograph.
3. Max and Gordy both want their own Dusty Field-autographed baseballs.	They sell 46 baseballs and save 2 for themselves.
4. Max and Gordy forget to save a baseball for Austin.	They buy a baseball with the money they earned.
5. Max and Gordy know that Austin is sad about not seeing Dusty Field.	They give Austin a new baseball autographed by Dusty Field.

At Home: Have the students think of problems they might have if they were home sick from school. Then have them write down ways that friends could help them.

Book 3.1/Unit 1
Max Malone   5

Story Elements

A **plot** is what happens in a story. The **characters** are who the story is about.
Read the story before you answer each question.

Tippy was a small brown dog. Fluffy was a black cat with
long hair. Both animals lived with their owner, Lisa. One day
Lisa let her pets out into the backyard. Both animals wanted to
see something new. Right away, Fluffy jumped over the fence.
Tippy dug a hole under the fence and crawled through.

Fluffy and Tippy happily ran from yard to yard. Suddenly a
big dog appeared. It was the largest, scariest dog Fluffy and
Tippy had ever seen. The dog barked and growled. Fluffy and
Tippy turned around and ran straight back to their yard.

1. Who are the main characters? _____ **Tippy, a dog and Fluffy, a cat** _____

   _____

2. What do the main characters want to do? _____ **see something new** _____

   _____

3. How are the characters able to do this? **Fluffy jumps over the fence,**

   and Tippy crawls under the fence to get out of the backyard.

4. What problem do Tippy and Fluffy run into? _____ **They meet a large dog**

   that growls at them.

5. What do the animals do next? **They run back to their own backyard.**

   _____

6. Do you think the animals learned anything from their experience?

   Answers may vary. Possible answer: Home is the best place to be.

6 Book 3.1/Unit 1
Max Malone

At Home: Have students draw pictures of other
things that could have happened in the story.

27

Compound Words

A **compound word** is made by joining two smaller words. The meanings of the two smaller words can help you figure out the meaning of the compound word.

Look at each of the compound words. Write the two words that make up each compound word. Then use the meanings of the two smaller words to write the meaning of the compound word.

popcorn

1. _____pop_____ + _____corn_____

2. meaning = _____corn that can be popped_____

homeland

3. _____home_____ + _____land_____

4. meaning = _____the land in which a person makes his or her home_____

sweatshirt

5. _____sweat_____ + _____shirt_____

6. meaning = _____a shirt that absorbs sweat_____

seacoast

7. _____sea_____ + _____coast_____

8. meaning = _____the place where the sea meets the land_____

sandbox

9. _____sand_____ + _____box_____

10. meaning = _____a box that holds sand_____

At Home: Ask students to name the short words in each of the following compound words: **steamship, grandfather, goldfish.**

McGraw-Hill School Division

Make Predictions

Read each selection. Then make **predictions** about what might happen based on the titles and stories.

Then answer the questions to predict an outcome.

Things That Snap and Bite

      Animal World is a safari park. You can drive through the park and see animals living freely, as they do in the wild. Be careful not to open your window! Some animals can be dangerous.

1. What kinds of animals do you predict live in Animal World?

   Answers would include animals that snap and bite, such as

   crocodiles, lions, and tigers.

2. Which parts of the story helped you make your prediction?

   The animals are wild. They snap and bite.

_____

Rufus to the Rescue

      My dog Rufus is so clever. Sometimes I think he actually understands what I am saying. Last week I got stuck climbing a tree. I shouted, "Rufus! Go home and fetch Dad!" Rufus barked at me and ran off.

3. What do you predict will happen? **Rufus will bring Dad back to help**

   the child stuck in the tree.

4. Which parts of the story helped you to predict your outcome?

   The title; also, Rufus is clever and seems to understand.

   He barked and ran off when the child asked him to get help.

4 Book 3.1/Unit 1
Champions of the World

At Home: Have students look at a book, magazine, or newspaper. Ask them to guess what the stories are about by looking at the titles.

29

Vocabulary

Choose the correct word from the box to complete each sentence. Then write the word on the line.

celebrated	cork	fans	pitcher	score	wrap

1. Kate ____celebrated____ her birthday by having a party.

2. A baseball's center is made out of ____cork____ .

3. Our ____pitcher____ threw the ball for the batter to hit.

4. The ____fans____ cheered when David stepped onto the stage.

5. I ____wrap____ the gift with colorful paper.

6. The goal tied the ____score____ between the two teams.

Write two sentences that use two of the vocabulary words in each sentence. **Answers will vary.**

7. _____

_____

_____

8. _____

_____

_____

At Home: Challenge students to write a short story about a sports event using three of the vocabulary words.

Fast Ball

Lou wanted to be a baseball player like his father. Long ago, Lou's father had been a *pitcher* on a winning team.

Pictures of Lou's father hung in Lou's bedroom. In one picture, *fans* cheered and *celebrated* as Lou's father threw the winning pitch. This pitch had made the *score* 3-0.

One afternoon, Lou went outside to practice. He wondered if he could pitch as well as his dad. It was cold, so he had to *wrap* a scarf around his neck. Then he threw the ball against a brick wall. Whack! The ball burst open and its *cork* fell out!

"Looks like I might be able to pitch", he thought. "I guess I'll give baseball a try!"

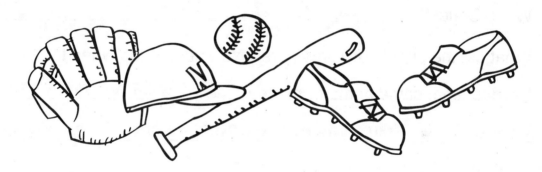

1. What is the name of the person who throws the ball to the batter?

   pitcher

2. What is inside a baseball?

   cork

3. What did Lou do with the scarf?

   He had to wrap it around his neck.

4. What was 3-0 in one of Lou's father's games?

   the score

5. What do you think Lou will do next in this story?

   He will join a baseball team.

At Home: Have students talk about games and sports they like. Also encourage them to talk about any sports or games any of their family members may play.

30A

McGraw-Hill School Division

Story Comprehension

1. What did the Toms River Little League team do? The team won the Little League World Championship in 1998.

2. What was the nickname for the Toms River team? "the Beast from the East"

3. What team did the Toms River team play against in the final game? a baseball team from Japan

4. How long had it been since a U.S. team had won the Little League World Series? five years, in 1993

5. What did the people of Toms River, New Jersey, do when the Little League team came home from the game? They had a parade to celebrate their team winning the world championship; the team rode on a fire truck.

6. What is special about Mark McGwire and Sammy Sosa? They both broke the old home run record the same year.

7. In your own words, tell about the home run record and how it was set. Answers will vary.

8. Is "Champions of the World" a true story? How do you know? Yes; it gives facts and information, instead of telling a story that a writer made up.

At Home: Have students look for pictures of people playing baseball. Then have them make a collage of pictures mixed with facts that they learned about baseball from reading "Champions of the World."

McGraw-Hill School Division

Use a Search Engine

Study the make-believe Web site addresses shown below. Use them to answer the questions below.

http://www.majorleaguebaseball.com/	http://www.bigleagueslugger.com/
http://www.baseballcamps.com/	http://www.baseballscholarships.com/
http://www.tomsriver.com/	http://www.halloffame.com/

Fill in the blank with a Web site address. Pick the Web site most likely to help you.

If you wanted information about:

1. a summer camp for baseball players

   http://www.baseballcamps.com/

2. big-league slugger baseball bats

   http://www.bigleagueslugger.com/

3. the Little League World Series champs from Toms River, New Jersey

   http://www.tomsriver.com/

4. a sports scholarship for playing baseball in college

   http://www.baseballscholarship.com/

5. next year's complete major-league baseball schedule

   http://www.majorleaguebaseball.com/

6. how to visit the Hall of Fame in Cooperstown, N.Y.

   http://www.halloffame.com/

Steps in a Process

Steps that you follow in order are called **steps in a process**. Writing down the steps in order will help you to remember them.

Think about the following activities. Each of them has several steps that need to be followed. Write down the steps in the process for each activity below. **Answers will vary. Possible examples follow.**

Find a book at the library.

1. Look up the number for the book.
2. Write down the number of the book.
3. Find the floor and bookshelf.
4. Locate the book that has the number.

Make a cup of chocolate milk.

1. Take the milk out of the refrigerator.
2. Take chocolate syrup from the cupboard.
3. Pour chocolate syrup into a glass.
4. Fill the rest of the glass with milk.
5. Stir it until it is mixed.

Make a costume for a costume party.

1. Decide which character you want to be.
2. Draw a picture of your costume.
3. Gather or buy materials and supplies.
4. Cut out the materials to be sewn together.
5. Sew your costume together.

McGraw-Hill School Division

At Home: Have students write down five steps that they follow when they do their homework.

Compound Words

You can figure out the meaning of a compound word by looking at the two smaller words within it and putting the two meanings together.

Below are definitions of some compound words. Complete the chart.

Definition	Compound Word	Two Words	
1. the town where a person makes his or her home	hometown	home	town
2. balls that are used to play the game of basketball	basketballs	basket	balls
3. made at home, not at a factory or a store	homemade	home	made
4. the place made for walking at the side of a road	sidewalk	side	walk
5. the days at the end of the school or work week	weekend	week	end
6. case to store books	bookcase	book	case

Book 3.1/Unit 1
Champions of the World

At Home: Ask students to name the compound word that means **the work that you do at school**.

Prefixes

A **prefix** is a word part that can be added to the beginning of a word to change the word's meaning. Knowing what a prefix means can help you figure out what a word means. The prefixes **un-** and **dis-** both mean "not" or "the opposite of."

Prefix + word	Meaning
dis + appears = disappears	the opposite of appears, to pass from sight
un + like = unlike	not alike, different

Write the prefix of each word. Write the word's meaning. Then use the word in a sentence of your own. **Answers will vary.**

1. **disagree**   Prefix: ___dis___ Meaning: <u>not agree, opposite of agree</u>

Sentence: _____

2. **unwrapped** Prefix: ___un___ Meaning: <u>not wrapped, opposite of</u>

<u>wrapped</u>

Sentence: _____

3. **disobey**   Prefix: ___dis___ Meaning: <u>opposite of obey, not obey</u>

Sentence: _____

4. **unlucky**   Prefix: ___un___ Meaning: <u>not lucky</u>

Sentence: _____

5. **displease** Prefix: ___dis___ Meaning: <u>opposite of please</u>

Sentence: _____

At Home: Ask students to name three other words that begin with the prefix **dis-** and then tell you their meanings.

35

Book 3.1/Unit 1
Champions of the World   10

Unit 1 Vocabulary Review

A. Read each word in Column 1. Then find a word in Column 2 that means the opposite. Write the letter of the word on the line.

<u>c</u> **1.** ceiling   **a.** wrong

<u>d</u> **2.** enormous   **b.** stop

<u>a</u> **3.** correct   **c.** floor

<u>e</u> **4.** within   **d.** tiny

<u>b</u> **5.** continue   **e.** outside

B. Supply the correct vocabulary word.

scene	journey	celebrated	gift
fans	cents	guard	

1. The _____fans_____ roared when Cora hit the home run.

2. Denny bought a _____gift_____ for his grandmother.

3. The _____journey_____ across the mountains took three days.

4. The large ball cost 75 _____cents_____ more than the small one.

5. The class _____celebrated_____ Leo's birthday by giving him a party.

6. When Jane saw the lovely _____scene_____, she wanted to paint a picture of it.

7. Harry and Jim stood _____guard_____ around the campfire.

12 Book 3.1/Unit 1
Unit 1 Vocabulary Review

At Home: Have students write a sentence for each vocabulary word in Part A.

36

Unit 1 Vocabulary Review

A. Answer each question.

1. **royal** Who might be members of a royal family?

   Sample answer: king, queen, prince, princess

2. **wrap** Why would someone wrap a package?

   Sample answer: to send it in the mail

3. **astonished** What amazing sight astonished you?

   Sample answer: a kitten as small as a mouse

4. **eager** What is something you would be eager to do?

   Sample answer: visit a friend

B. Write the vocabulary word that means almost the same as the underlined word.

section	scattered	enormous	unusual	straighten	gift

1. That kind of stone is very rare. _____ **unusual**

2. Wally finished the first part of the book. _____ **section**

3. Janet spread the seeds on the soil. _____ **scattered**

4. Nancy will fix the crooked picture. _____ **straighten**

5. The Statue of Liberty is huge. _____ **enormous**

6. My friend gave me a wonderful present. _____ **gift**

At Home: Have students write a question for each vocabulary word in Part B. Then answer the question. Use Part A as a guide.

Book 3.1/Unit 1
Unit 1 Vocabulary Review   10

McGraw-Hill School Division

Cause and Effect

The person, thing or event that makes something happen is called the **cause**. The **effect** is what happens, or the result of that cause.

Read each cause. Then choose the correct effect from the box and write it on the line.

Effects

The cake got burned.

She decided to call the garage for help.

The plow trucks were busy.

She ran out of food for her guests.

The students went outside to play.

---

1. **Cause:** The school bell rang.

   Effect: The students went outside to play.

2. **Cause:** Anna's car made a lot of strange noises.

   Effect: She decided to call the garage for help.

3. **Cause:** Jay fell asleep while his cake was in the oven.

   Effect: The cake got burned.

4. **Cause:** More people came to Amanda's party than she expected.

   Effect: She ran out of food for her guests.

5. **Cause:** It snowed for twelve hours.

   Effect: The plow trucks were busy.

5 Book 3.1/Unit 2
City Green

At Home: Have students tell you some of the effects that could be caused by a rainy day.

38

Vocabulary

Decide whether each statement is **true** or **false**.
Explain the false statements.

1. There is still room left in a bucket that is filled *halfway*.

   True

2. *Excitement* usually causes people to fall asleep.

   False; it usually stirs people up.

3. A big pile of things is called a *heap*.

   True

4. *Stems* are the part of a flower that grow out of the ground.

   True

5. When a train is running on *schedule*, it is going to arrive at the station very late.

   False; the train will arrive on time.

6. A picnic *area* is a space set aside where people can eat.

   True

McGraw-Hill School Division

Andrew's Award

The school awards show was *halfway* over. So far the program had perfectly followed the printed *schedule*. Andrew felt so much *excitement* that he paced back and forth. He was in the *area* where all the award winners waited.

Early in the school year, Andrew had collected used cans. He brought them to a place where a city worker counted them. Then the worker threw them into a big *heap* of other used cans.

Andrew received twenty dollars for the used cans. With the money, he bought flowers to plant in front of the school. By the day of the awards, the *stems* were just beginning to pop up from the ground.

1. Where did the city worker throw Andrew's cans?

   <u>into a heap</u>

2. What did Andrew feel at the awards show?

   <u>excitement</u>

3. Where did Andrew pace back and forth?

   <u>in the area where the award winners waited</u>

4. What part of the flowers were beginning to pop up?

   <u>the stems</u>

5. Why was Andrew winning an award?

   <u>He spent the money he made on planting flowers for his school.</u>

 5 Book 3.1/Unit 2
City Green

At Home: Invite students to talk about what they would do to help their school look nice.

39A

Story Comprehension

Think about "City Green." Then complete the chart below.
Answers may vary.

1. **Setting of the Story:** a city neighborhood _____

2. **Main Characters:** Marcy, Old Man Hammer, Miss Rosa, Marcy's

   mother and brother _____

Beginning of the Story

3. An old building was torn down, leaving behind an empty city lot.

4. The empty lot became filled with trash and litter.

5. Old Man Hammer said nothing good will ever come of the empty lot.

Middle of the Story

6. Marcy and Miss Rosa passed around a petition to lease the lot

   from the city.

7. Everyone in the neighborhood helped to clean up the lot and plant

   a garden.

8. One night, Marcy saw Old Man Hammer planting seeds in the

   garden.

End of the Story

9. Marcy begged Old Man Hammer to come see his seedlings in the

   garden.

10. When summer came, Marcy and Old Man Hammer enjoyed sitting

   in the garden near the sunflowers.

At Home: Have students identify and discuss problems
on their street or in their own community.

Book 3.1/Unit 2
City Green
10

Use a Telephone Directory

102   Garage Doors—Gas

Garage Doors
Clegg Brothers
        45 Simpson St 555–3423
T.J.'s Garage Supplies
        523 Maple Ln 555–6520
Garbage Removal
        See Rubbish and Garbage Removal
Garden Centers—plants, supplies
Chestnut Hill Farms
        456 Harrison Blvd 555–0456
Harry's Garden World
        Route 5 + Gray Way 555–4589
        Montclair Mall 555–1111
Garden Furniture
Chestnut Hill Farms
        456 Harrison Blvd 555–0456
Moon River Junction
        626 Good Hope Rd 555–8734

Pretend you're building a garden. Use the section of the Yellow Pages shown here to help you.

1. Which two stores sell plants? <u>Chestnut Hill Farms,</u>

    <u>Harry's Garden World</u>

2. Which store sells both both plants and garden furniture?

    <u>Chestnut Hill Farms</u>

3. What's the phone number of Moon River Junction? <u>555-8734</u>

4. Pretend you need to remove garbage from your garden. Where would

    you look in these Yellow Pages? <u>Rubbish and Garbage Removal</u>

5. Which two stores sell garage doors?

    <u>Clegg Brothers and T.J.'s Garage Supplies</u>

5   Book 3.1/Unit 2
    City Green

At Home: Ask students to explain why they would not
find listings of stores that sell fans on this page.

41

Cause and Effect

Events in a story can often be organized by **cause** and **effect**. One event causes another to happen. Write the cause or effect of each event in the chart below. **Answers may vary.**

Story Event (Cause)	Story Event (Effect)
Marcy asked Old Man Hammer about the building that used to be on the lot.	1. Old Man Hammer told her to "Scram!"
Spring came.	2. Miss Rosa started cleaning coffee cans.
3. Old Man Hammer told Marcy and Miss Rosa that the lot had plenty of dirt.	Marcy and Miss Rosa dug for dirt in the empty lot. They got the idea to turn the lot into a garden.
Marcy, Miss Rosa, and other people from the block passed around a petition.	4. They got enough signatures to rent the lot from the city for one dollar.
5. Neighbors saw that the group was cleaning up the lot.	Everyone pitched in to help clean the lot.
6. Marcy saw Old Man Hammer plant seeds in the garden.	Marcy patted the neat and tidy garden row for good luck.
Marcy saw the tiny green shoots of Old Man Hammer's seeds sprouting in the garden.	7. Marcy brought Old Man Hammer to see the seedlings.
Summer came, and in the back of the garden grew a tall patch of sunflowers.	8. Marcy and Old Man Hammer sat in the garden and enjoyed the sunflowers that he planted.

At Home: Have students write a paragraph explaining the possible effect that the garden had on Old Man Hammer's life.

42

Book 3.1/Unit 2
City Green

8

Draw Conclusions

To draw a **conclusion** about a character or an event in a story, you use facts from the story. You also use your own knowledge and experience. Drawing conclusions as you read can help you better understand a story.

Answer each question below. Base your conclusion on your own experience and on information from "City Green." **Answers may vary.**

1. What kind of person is Marcy?

   She is friendly, thoughtful, concerned, and involved with her

   neighborhood.

2. What details from the selection helped you to draw that conclusion?

   She knew everyone and kept trying to be friends with Old Man

   Hammer.

3. What kind of relationship did Old Man Hammer and his neighbors have?

   Not very friendly.

4. What details from the selection helped you to draw your conclusion?

   Old Man Hammer hollered "scram" to Marcy when she asked him

   a question. He yelled to the neighbors that they were all wasting

   their time working to build the community garden.

5. Why did Old Man Hammer secretly plant seeds?

   The old building meant a lot to him. Deep down inside, he was

   really a nice man.

6. What details from the selection helped you draw that conclusion?

   He used to live there; he sat with Rosa in the finished garden.

6 | Book 3.1/Unit 2
City Green

At Home: Have students draw a conclusion about
the effect the community garden had on the
neighborhood.

43

Context Clues

When you read an unfamiliar word you can use **context clues**, or the words or sentences before or after the word, to help you determine the word's meaning.

Read the sentence or sentences. Use context clues to figure out the meaning of the underlined words. Write the meaning of each word. **Answers will vary.**

1. The mother whale takes good care of its <u>calf</u> after it is born.

   calf means <u>baby whale or animal</u>

2. People joined together to <u>rescue</u> the whale when it was in trouble.

   rescue means <u>save</u>

3. The whales <u>migrate</u> from the north each winter and swim to the warm waters in the south. They return to the north again each summer.

   migrate means <u>travel, travel each season</u>

4. Many save-the-whale groups are working to protect these big <u>creatures</u> of the sea.

   creatures means <u>animals</u>

5. Blue whales are <u>mammoth</u> and can grow to one hundred feet.

   mammoth means <u>huge</u>

At Home: Have students point out the context clues in each sentence that helped them to determine the meaning of each word.

44

Book 3.1/Unit 2
City Green

5

Compare and Contrast

Read each object name. Answer the questions about each object to complete the chart. Write **Y** for **yes**. Write **N** for **no**.

    A.

Is it	white?	round?	food?	fun?	hard?
baseball	Y	Y	N	Y	Y
onion	Y	Y	Y	N	Y
snowball	Y	Y	N	Y	Y
soap bubble	N	Y	N	Y	N

    B. Use the completed chart to think about how the objects are alike and how they are different.

1. In what ways is the soap bubble different from the other objects?

   It is not white, and it is not hard.

2. How are snowballs and onions different?

   You eat onions, but not snowballs; snowballs melt.

3. How are baseballs and snowballs alike?

   You can throw both of them.

4. In what way are all 5 objects alike?

   They are all round.

At Home: Have students add one more question to the chart. How do the objects compare using this new trait?

Vocabulary

Write the letter of the word that best matches each definition.

1. When you have exchanged one thing for another,   **a.** peaks

   you have ___c___ it.

2. When the water in a stream has moved   **b.** handful

   smoothly, it has ___f___.

3. Hard, tiny pieces of things like rock or sand are   **c.** traded

   known as ___e___.

4. The amount you can hold in one hand is a ___b___.   **d.** canyons

5. The pointed tops of mountains are called ___a___.   **e.** grains

6. Deep valleys with steep sides are known as ___d___.   **f.** flowed

Book 3.1/Unit 2
The Sun, the Wind and the Rain   6

A Mountain of Fun

Molly mixed paper, paste, and water. She wanted to use the material to make something. "I will make two mountains with tall *peaks*," she said. When the mountains were finished, Cliff placed sand in the *canyons* between the mountains. It took a large *handful* of sand to completely cover the canyon floor. "The *grains* will stick to the sticky surface and look like the dirt of a canyon," Cliff told Molly.

Next, Molly painted the mountain gray and Cliff painted the canyon brown. Then they *traded* places and added on another layer of paint.

Molly and Cliff stepped back to look at their finished model. There was just one thing missing. Molly knew what it was. Slowly she painted a strip of blue through the canyon. The water looked like it *flowed* .

1. What is another word for the top of a mountain?

   the peak

2. Where did Cliff place sand?

   in the canyons

3. How much sand did Cliff use?

   a handful

4. What did the blue that Molly painted onto the model look like?

   flowing water

5. What did Molly do to help make the model?

   She made the mountains and painted on the water.

At Home: Encourage students to name any famous mountains or canyons they know about. Where are they? Have they ever been to them?

46A

Story Comprehension

Answer the following questions about "The Sun, the Wind and the Rain."

1. Where does this story take place? **The story takes place by**

   the ocean and on the beach.

2. What two mountains are looked at in the story? **The mountains are**

   the earth mountain and Elizabeth's sand mountain.

3. What kind of information does the story tell about the real mountain?

   The story tells about the way that the mountain is built and

   the way it breaks apart.

4. What happens when rivers rush down the earth mountain? **The rivers**

   cut valleys into the mountain and grind the rocks into pebbles.

5. What makes Elizabeth cry? **Elizabeth cries when rain begins to**

   destroy her sand mountain.

6. Why don't either of the mountains stay the same? **The sun, the wind,**

   and the rain break them apart.

At Home: Have students draw a picture of one of the scenes described in "The Sun, the Wind, and the Rain."

47

Book 3.1/Unit 2
The Sun, the Wind and the Rain

6

Use a Dictionary

Place each of the dictionary parts below in its proper place.

> sizzle
> *adjective*
> sidewalk
> to make music with your voice
> SIDE
> (sīz)

1. _____SIDE_____ —SIZZLE

2. _____sidewalk_____ 1. a path by the side of a street (sīd'wôk) *noun*

3. **silly** 1. lacking common sense, foolish (sil'ē) ___*adjective*___

4. **sing** 1. __to make music with your voice_____

    (sing) *verb*

5. **size** 1. the amount of space an object takes up ____(sīz)____ *noun*

6. _____sizzle_____ 1. to make a hissing sound (siz'əl) *verb*

6 Book 3.1/Unit 2
The Sun, the Wind and the Rain

At Home: Ask students to look up the word silt and to put it in its proper place in the above dictionary page, writing in the definition, pronunciation, and part of speech.

48

Compare and Contrast

Think about "The Sun, the Wind and the Rain." In what ways are the earth mountain and Elizabeth's mountain alike? How are they different? Complete the chart to compare the two mountains.

	earth mountain	**Elizabeth's mountain**
Formed when?	long ago	built today
Made of what?	rock and sandstone	wet sand
How big?	reaching up into the sky	as tall as a child
Rain does what?	destroys it and carries it to sea	destroys it and carries it to sea

Why do you think the author wrote about the two kinds of mountains? Circle your answer.

- to show how big they are

- to show mountain canyons

- to show how mountains change over time

At Home: Have students share experiences they have had at the beach or the mountains. Encourage them to focus on the sights and sounds.

49

Book 3.1/Unit 2
The Sun, the Wind and the Rain
5

Draw Conclusions

A conclusion is what you decide after you have read a story. You can also use your own experience to help you **draw conclusions**.

Draw your conclusions about the story by answering each question. **Answers may vary.**

Annie took a lot of pictures. There was one rock that looked like a bridge and another that looked like a wise old owl.

Annie wondered out loud if people had ever lived in this wonderful place.

"I'll show you something and you can decide for yourself," her father said.

It was already getting dark when they parked the car next to an enormous rock. Annie was astonished to see drawings of the horses and people.

"Native Americans made these pictures hundreds of years ago. Aren't they beautiful?" Annie's father said.

"Can we come back tomorrow when it's light enough for me to take a picture?"

1. Do you think Annie enjoyed her trip? _____ **yes**

2. What information from the story helped you to draw your conclusion?

   She took pictures of the rocks; she liked the pictures on the rock;

   she said it was a wonderful place.

3. Where might Annie and her father be? **Definitely in America,**

   because "Native Americans" made the pictures on the wall,

   maybe in the West.

4. Had people ever lived in the place Annie visited? Explain. **Yes, people**

   made pictures on the wall hundreds of years ago.

At Home: Have students draw conclusions about whether or not Annie's father had ever visited this place before.

Antonyms and Synonyms

Antonyms are words that have the opposite, or nearly opposite, meaning.

Synonyms are words that have the same, or nearly the same, meaning.

Antonyms	**Synonyms**
hot, cold	large, big

Choose a word from the list on the right that is a synonym or antonym for the word on the left. Write the word on the first line. On the second line, write **S** if the word pairs are synonyms. Write **A** if the word pairs are antonyms.

1. shout	yell	S		different
2. like	dislike	A		won
3. help	aid	S		distrust
4. less	more	A		dislike
5. noisy	quiet	A		yell
6. unusual	different	S		quiet
7. believe	distrust	A		down
8. lost	won	A		aid
9. angry	mad	S		more
10. up	down	A		mad

At Home: Have students name a synonym and an antonym for **chilly.**

Cause and Effect

A **cause** is what makes something happen. The **effect** is what happens as a result of the cause. You can use cause and effect to help you make predictions about what might happen next.

Read each paragraph. Write the cause that made the effect happen. Then write a sentence to make a prediction. **Predictions may vary.**

Jack grew apples to sell at the market. This year the apples were perfect. They had not been eaten by worms. Jack had found a new way to keep the worms away.

1. **Cause:** Jack had used a new way to keep the worms away.

2. **Effect:** The apples were perfect and hadn't been filled with worms.

3. **Predict** what Jack will do next year: He may sell his idea for keeping worms away to other apple farmers.

Anna decided to eat her lunch outside. She sat on a bench and took out her sandwich. Suddenly she heard a buzzing sound. There was a bee flying around Anna. The bee wanted a bite of her sandwich.

4. **Cause:** Anna takes out her sandwich.

5. **Effect:** A bee is buzzing around Anna.

6. **Predict** what Anna will do for lunch tomorrow: She may eat her sandwich inside.

Vocabulary

Identify and write down clues to the meaning of the underlined word in each question.

1. The buffalo, a large, furry animal with a hump on its back, is in danger of becoming extinct. **large, furry animal with a hump on its back**

2. The darkness of night was all around us, and there was no light to be seen. **night, no light**

3. Did the way the echoes of my voice bounced off the mountain make me seem far away? **bounced off the mountain**

4. As groups of animals traveled together across the plains, the noise the herd made was like thunder. **groups of animals traveled together**

5. The berries were ripe and juicy now that they were ready to eat. **juicy, ready to eat**

6. To protect themselves from the sun, the two girls decided to shelter under a beach umbrella. **to protect themselves from the sun, under a beach umbrella**

At Home: Have students make up a crossword puzzle using the vocabulary words. Have them write a clue for each word.

53

Book 3.1/Unit 2
Dream Wolf

6

McGraw-Hill School Division

A Return to Home

Long ago, a young *buffalo* walked across the Great Plains. As *darkness* came, she began to look for *shelter*. The buffalo called out for someone to help her find a place to sleep. But all she could hear were the *echoes* of her own voice.

The buffalo grew hungry. She ate some sweet, *ripe* berries. She also ate some small plants.

Suddenly, she saw another buffalo. She followed the other buffalo. The buffalo led her to a place where several *herds* rested together.

When some of the herd saw the newcomer, they gave her food. They also made a space where she could sleep.

1. What did the *buffalo* begin to look for?

   shelter

2. What did the *buffalo* hear when she called out?

   the echoes of her own voice

3. Why were the berries the *buffalo* ate sweet?

   They were ripe.

4. In what kind of groups do *buffalo* live?

   herds

5. Why did the young *buffalo* follow the other *buffalo*?

   She hoped he would lead her to shelter.

Story Comprehension

Think about the story of Tiblo and Tanksi in "Dream Wolf." Then answer each question below. **Answers will vary.**

QUESTIONS	ANSWERS
SETTINGS Where does the story take place?	1. the hills 2. the wolf's den 3. camp
CHARACTERS Who are the main characters?	4. Tiblo 5. Tanksi 6. the wolf
PLOT What problem do Tiblo and Tanksi face?	7. When they climb into the hills, they become lost.
EVENTS Where do Tiblo and Tanksi spend the night? What happens there? What happens when Tiblo wakes up and sees the wolf?	8. They spend the night in a wolf's cave. Tiblo dreams about a wolf, who really does sleep with them and keeps them warm. 9. Tiblo asks the wolf to help them find the way back to camp.
CONCLUSION How does the story end?	10. The wolf leads them back to camp, where everyone is happy to see them.

At Home: Have students illustrate a scene from "Dream Wolf."

Use an Encyclopedia

Natural Bridge—Navigation

Natural Bridge is a bridge made from stone by nature. Wind or rain or rivers carved away the stone over many years. Usually softer stone is removed from under harder stone. A bridge of harder stone is all that remains.

Nauru is a small island country in the Pacific Ocean. It is the third smallest nation in the world. Monaco and Vatican City are smaller. It's greatest resource is phosphate, a substance used to make fertilizer.

Navajo, a Native American group who have lived in the southwestern United States since around 1000 A.D. They are the largest Native American group in the United States. Many members still live in houses called hogans, made of earth and logs. See also Indian, American

Naval Reserve. See Navy, United States

Fill in the blank spaces below based on the encyclopedia page.

Entry Words:

Natural bridge

Nauru

Navajo

Naval Reserve

Cross-References:

See also Indian, American

See Navy, United States

Guide Words:

Natural bridge

navigation

At Home: Ask students if they would look on this page for information about narwhal whales. Why or why not?

Cause and Effect

In "Dream Wolf," things happen that cause other events to occur. Answer the following questions about **cause** and **effect**.

1. Why do the people move from the plains to the hills and valleys?

   The berry bushes are ripe in the valleys.

2. What did Tiblo do when he became tired of picking

   berries? He decided to sneak off into the hills with Tanksi.

3. What effect did the sun going down have on the two children?

   They got lost.

4. While the children slept, a wolf came into the cave and kept them

   warm. What effect did this have on Tiblo's dreams? It caused Tiblo

   to have a dream about a wolf.

5. The wolf led the children back to their camp. What did the children

   then ask the wolf? They asked the wolf to live with them.

6. What did the people in the camp do when they saw the children

   coming down the hill? They galloped out on horses to bring the

   children home.

7. What has caused wolves to disappear from the hills where they used to

   live? Hunters have killed the wolves and driven them away.

8. When do the people say the wolves will return? When we have

   the wolves in our hearts and dreams again.

McGraw-Hill School Division

Compare and Contrast

When you **compare** and **contrast** two things, you point out how they are the same and how they are different.

Look at the picture. Then answer the questions. **Answers may vary.**

1. Name two ways that Sam and Frankie look alike. **They are both dogs; they both have four legs and shaggy hair.**

2. Name two ways that Sam and Frankie look different. **Sam is taller than Frankie; Sam has spots while Frankie is one color; Sam has small pointed ears while Frankie's ears are long and droopy.**

3. What is the same about what the two dogs are doing? **They are both chewing on something.**

4. What is different about what the two dogs are doing? **Sam is chewing a bone while Frankie is chewing a ball.**

At Home: Have students organize their observations of Sam and Frankie into a two-column chart. Label the columns "Alike" and "Different."

Context Clues

Context clues are words or sentences that can help you find the meaning of an unfamiliar word. You may find context clues in the text before or after the unfamiliar word.

Read the selection. Write a definition for each word or term.

There are more kinds of plants and animals living in the warm, wet rain forests than anywhere else on Earth. It is interesting to know how a rain forest works and why it is always so moist. The leaves of the trees catch rain. The rain then travels down the stems to the ground. The ground absorbs most of the water and the rest goes into rivers and streams. Under the ground, the roots of the trees absorb the water in the soil. Then the roots send the water up the trunk of each tree, out into its branches, and into its leaves. If you stand on the ground in a rain forest and look up, all you can see is leaves. The trees' leaves collect so much water that clouds form above them. The clouds fall again as rain. When it rains, the pattern begins all over again, with the leaves catching the rain.

1. **rain forest**   a warm, wet forest where many different

      kinds of plants and animals live

2. **moist**   damp, wet

3. **absorbs**   soak up, take in

4. **soil**   earth

5. **pattern**   something that happens over and over

      again

58   **At Home:** Ask students to use some of the new words
      in sentences.

Book 3.1/Unit 2   5
Dream Wolf

McGraw-Hill School Division

Important and Unimportant Information

When you read nonfiction, you need to be able to tell the difference between passages that include **important information**, or facts, about the main idea and passages that give **unimportant information**. Unimportant information does not add details about the main idea, although it may include interesting observations.

Read the following story. Draw a line under each sentence that contains important information about sea horses.

Sea Horses

"What kind of horse has no hair?" A sea horse, of course.

Sea horses live in warm water that is not very deep. They eat tiny things in the water that people cannot even see, as well as small fish. Not many fish like to eat sea horses though. They have too many bones.

Sea horses are clever artists. They turn into the colors of the plants around them so that they can hide from fish that hunt them. It would be wonderful to see a sea horse change from brown to yellow!

Copy a sentence that includes **unimportant** information. Then explain why the sentence does not add important information about sea horses.

Possible answer: "What kind of horse has no hair?" This

sentence does not give any factual information.

_____

_____

Book 3.1/Unit 2
Spiders at Work

At Home: Have students explain how they determined which information was important to learning about sea horses.

59

Vocabulary

Supply the correct word from the list to complete each sentence.

ruin   liquid   capture   serious   skills   struggles

1. A spider builds a web because it wants to catch, or

   _____**capture**_____ , insects.

2. If you roll around on the grass in your best clothes, you might

   _____**ruin**_____ them.

3. A _____**serious**_____ problem needs to be thought about deeply

   and carefully.

4. When a fly _____**struggles**_____ to escape from a spider's

   web, it makes a great effort to try and get free.

5. Water is a_____**liquid**_____ , but ice is not.

6. Playing the piano and drawing are two _____**skills**_____ that I

   have mastered.

At Home: Have students write a short story using three
or more of the vocabulary words.

Book 3.1/Unit 2
Spiders at Work 6

McGraw-Hill School Division

Brave Little Spider

Little May was very *serious* about becoming a web spinner. There was one problem, though. She just didn't have the *skills*. Every time May tried to build a web, she would *ruin* it one way or another. "My poor little girl *struggles* so much," said her mother.

One day, a little boy tried to *capture* May's mother by putting her into a jar. May didn't know what to do. Then she had an idea! Quickly she began to spin a web over a small puddle of *liquid*.

As the boy walked through the web he lost his balance and fell. May and her mother were able to escape. May's mother was proud of her daughter. "Your webs might not be strong enough to catch bugs," May's mother said. "But they sure are strong enough to save me!"

1. How did May feel about wanting to be a web spinner?

   serious

2. What does May need to have to become a web spinner?

   skills

3. What does the little boy try to do?

   He tries to capture May's mother.

4. Where did May spin her web to help her mother?

   over a puddle of liquid

5. How did May's mother feel about May at the end of the story?

   She was proud of May for being brave enough to save her.

5 Book 3.1/Unit 2
Spiders at Work

At Home: Have students use the italicized words
from the story in sentences.

60A

Story Comprehension

Use the story "Spiders at Work" to help you answer these questions.

1. How many legs does a spider have? **eight legs**

2. What is a bridge line? **A bridge line is the first line in a spider's web.**

3. How can you tell if a spider is a black widow? **Black widows have shiny black bodies with a red or yellow mark on the bottom.**

4. Why do people need to look out for black widow spiders? **Black widows have a poisonous bite.**

5. What kind of spiders do some people keep as pets? **tarantulas**

6. How did the daddy-longlegs get its name? **It has very long legs.**

7. Name some places that spiders can be found. **They can be found all over the world, including jungles, mountains, up in the sky, and even out at sea.**

8. According to a Navaho folk tale, what did Spider Woman teach the Navaho people to do? **She taught them how to spin wool into thread and weave it into blankets.**

At Home: Ask students to imagine what it would be like to be a spider. Have them write a short story about a day as a spider.

61

Book 3.1/Unit 2
Spiders at Work

8

McGraw-Hill School Division

Use a Dictionary

The word-history section of a dictionary entry tells how the word entered our language. *ME* stands for Middle English, an older form of English. *OE* stands for Old English, an even older form of English. *Fr* stands for French, and *OFr* stands for old French. Latin is also an old language.

leg the part of the body that is used for standing or walking *noun* (leg) ME *leggr.*

capture to grab or hold *verb* (kap´ chər) OFr< Latin *captura*

insect a small animal without a backbone *noun* (in sekt´) Latin *insectum*

spin to turn around and around *verb* (spin) ME *spinnen*

weave to spin a web or cocoon *verb* (wēv) OE *wefan*

Fill in the blanks in the chart below.

WORD	PRONUNCIATION	DEFINITION	PART OF SPEECH	ORIGIN
leg	(leg)	the part of the body that is used for standing or walking	noun	ME *leggr*
spin	(spin)	to turn around and around	verb	ME *spinnen*
weave	(wēv)	to spin a web or cocoon	verb	OE *wefan*
insect	(in'sekt)	a type of small animal without a backbone	noun	Latin *insectum*
capture	(kap´ cher)	to grab or hold	verb	OFr< Latin *captura*

Important and Unimportant Information

People often read stories like "Spiders at Work" in order to answer questions that they have. Keeping such purposes in mind can help you sort out **important information** from **unimportant information**.

Decide whether or not each statement below is important to the given purpose. Write an **X** next to the information that is important.

Purpose: To find out which spiders can hurt people

____ **1.** The web looks pretty, but it is a trap for flies and other bugs.

_X_ **2.** Black widow spiders do not bite people very often.

_X_ **3.** The tarantula's bite is about as strong as a bee sting.

____ **4.** Spiders belong to a family of their own.

Purpose: To find out how a spider builds its web

_X_ **5.** The air helps the spider by blowing the bridge line from one plant to another.

____ **6.** Daddy-longlegs eat flies and mosquitoes.

_X_ **7.** The spider keeps building by going back and forth, and up and down.

_X_ **8.** The spider spins a sticky thread in a circle.

Purpose: To find out where spiders live

____ **9.** Some spiders are as small as the head of a pin.

_X_ **10.** Water spiders have their homes under water.

____ **11.** Ants have six legs, and spiders have eight legs.

_X_ **12.** One spider in South America lives in trees and eats small birds.

At Home: Ask students to illustrate one of the sentences on the page.

Book 3.1/Unit 2
Spiders at Work
12

Draw Conclusions

You can **draw conclusions** based on information from a story or from your own life. You can often draw conclusions from just a few clues.

Draw a conclusion from each passage below.

1. Sometimes, Jeff and Bill would fight over their toys. When this happened, their grandmother played games with them so they would forget why they were fighting.

   Conclusion: What can you tell about the boys' grandmother?

   <u>**She is patient and knows how to keep children from fighting.**</u>

2. The flowers had just started to peek out from beneath the ground. The park was full of people wearing jackets and hats that they didn't need.

   Conclusion: What time of year is it? How do you know? <u>**Spring;**</u>

   <u>**the flowers are coming up and the weather is warm.**</u>

3. Kim decided to try out for the baseball team. Her brother said she was better than he had been at her age.

   Conclusion: Is Kim's brother older or younger? _____**older**_____

4. "It is too bad that so many people are afraid of spiders. Most spiders don't bite! Many are even helpful. They eat bugs that might bite you," said Jack.

   Conclusion: How does Jack feel about spiders? <u>**He likes spiders.**</u>

5. May spilled her milk. Her teacher still had something kind to say about May. May's teacher was good when things went wrong.

   Conclusion: What is May's teacher like? <u>**She is kind.**</u>

McGraw-Hill School Division

Antonyms and Synonyms

Antonyms are words with opposite meanings.
Synonyms are words with the same or similar meanings.

Replace the underlined word with a synonym. Write the answer on the line. **Answers may vary.**

1. The class was excited about going on the trip. _outing_____

2. They asked their relatives for help. _families_____

3. It is silent in the park at night. _quiet_____

4. They were curious to learn about the animals. _interested_____

Write an antonym for each underlined word. **Answers may vary.**

5. The campers were unprepared when the storm appeared.

   ready_____

6. They did not want to spend all night in their tents.

   day_____

7. After a brief shower, the ground was soaked.

   long_____

8. Everyone wondered if the rain would continue.

   stop_____

At Home: Ask students to form antonyms for **usual, happy,** and **pleased** by adding the prefix **un-** or **dis-** to each word.

65

Book 3.1/Unit 2
Spiders at Work

8

Compare and Contrast

Read the list of animals. Use what you know to fill in the chart.
Answers may vary.

| hamsters | dogs | goats | frogs | geese | parrots | rabbits |
| goldfish | cats | ducks | sheep | horses | lizards | canaries |

Favorite Animals

May Live on Farms	May Live in Homes	Can Swim	Can Fly
goats	hamsters	ducks	geese
geese	parrots	goldfish	ducks
ducks	rabbits	frogs	parrots
sheep	lizards		canaries
horses	dogs		
rabbits	cats		

Choose two animals from the chart. Write how they are alike and how they are different.

Possible answer: Goats and geese may live on farms. Geese can fly, but goats cannot.

_____

_____

_____

At Home: Have students compare and contrast two of the animals on the chart. Have them look at such topics as size, weight, and temperament.

Vocabulary

Supply the correct words from the list to complete each sentence.
The same vocabulary word is used twice in each example.

crops   earthquake   hatch   respect   soldiers   woven

1. _____Crops_____ are plants we grow for food. Wheat and corn are

   two kinds of _____crops_____ farmers grow in the United States.

2. When the ground started to shake, I knew we were having an

   _____earthquake_____ . Luckily, no one was hurt during the

   _____earthquake_____ , but some buildings were damaged.

3. The hen sits on her eggs to keep them warm until they

   _____hatch_____ . Watch the eggs _____hatch_____ to see the

   little chicks!

4. I really admire and _____respect_____ Mrs. Jackson. As one of the best

   teachers at school, she has earned everyone's _____respect_____ .

5. My cousins joined the army because they wanted to be

   _____soldiers_____ . Besides fighting in wars, _____soldiers_____

   also help to protect and rebuild cities and countries.

6. Some of the most beautiful blankets in the world are _____woven_____

   by Native Americans. Yarn is carefully _____woven_____ together in

   different colored strips to make lovely patterns.

At Home: Have students use each vocabulary word in
another sentence.

McGraw-Hill School Division

Two Birds in the Hand

Two *soldiers* were marching through a field. The men were returning to their families. They had been helping people recover from an *earthquake*.

Suddenly the soldiers heard a sound. On the edge of a row of *crops* they found a bird's nest. One little bird was about to *hatch*. Another was already out. There was no mother bird. For several minutes the men waited for the mother bird. Finally, they realized that the baby birds were alone.

"Poor little birds," said one soldier. He placed the nest inside his big *woven* coat. "I will take them home."

"You are a great man," said the other soldier. "You *respect* all life, no matter how big or small!"

1. Where did the soldiers find the bird's nest?

   <u>on the edge of a row of crops</u>

2. What in the story was *woven*?

   <u>the soldier's coat</u>

3. What was one little bird about to do?

   <u>hatch</u>

4. What had the soldiers been doing at the beginning of the story?

   <u>helping people recover from an earthquake</u>

5. Why did the soldier feel sorry for the birds?

   <u>They did not have a mother.</u>

5   Book 3.1/Unit 2
    Web Wonders

At Home: Help students think about and discuss why baby animals might need help to survive.

67A

Story Comprehension

Answer the following questions about "Web Wonders."

1. Stories may be written to give information, to entertain, or both. Why do you think this story was written? **Answers may vary:**

   both to inform and to entertain

2. In the story, why did enemy arrows bounce off Genghis Khan's soldiers? **because spider silk was woven into their clothes**

3. Do you think this story is true? Why or why not? **Answers may vary: It may be true since spider silk is known to be very strong.**

4. How can baby spiders travel so far? **They spin a long silk line, and the wind carries them.**

5. Why can't farmers raise spiders for their silk? **because spiders eat each other**

6. If scientists could make something as strong as spider's silk, what would they use it for?

   car bumpers, jeans, in bridges

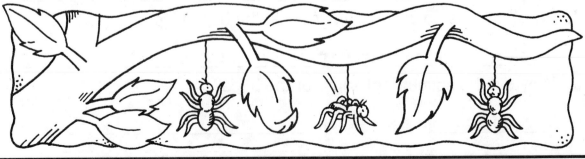

At Home: Ask students to explain why scientists are interested in making humanmade spider silk. Have students suggest some other possible uses for it.

Book 3.1/Unit 2
Web Wonders

6

Use a Resource

Study the sample dictionary entry. Then take a careful look at the encyclopedia entry that is below it.

nylon a strong fabric manufactured from chemicals. Nylon is used to make thread, clothes, stockings, tires for automobiles, tents for camping, and many other things. **ny-lon** (nī′lon) *noun.*

nylon is the family name for a group of materials made from chemicals. Coal, water, and chemicals are blended to make a wide variety of products. Nylon can be both strong and flexible. In 1937, it was first used to replace silk in stockings. Wallace Carothers developed special ways to make nylon for the Dupont Company. The first nylon he produced melted at low temperatures. If you made a dress out of this early nylon, a hot iron would melt it. By adding other chemicals, the nylon we know today was created. Qiana is a type of nylon that is commonly used in modern clothes. It has many of the qualities of silk.

Now read the selections below. Decide if they might have come from a dictionary entry or an encyclopedia entry. Write *dictionary* or *encyclopedia* to answer the questions below.

1. Which resource tells the history of *nylon*?

   <u>encyclopedia</u>

2. Which resource defines *nylon* as a strong fabric manufactured from chemicals? <u>dictionary</u>

3. Which resource tells you how to pronounce *nylon*?

   <u>dictionary</u>

4. Which resource tells you about a type of *nylon* called Qiana?

   <u>encyclopedia</u>

5. Which resource tells you that *nylon* is a noun?

   <u>dictionary</u>

5 Book 3.1/Unit 2
Web Wonders

At Home: Ask students where they might look to find predictions about how nylon will be used in the future.

69

Important and Unimportant Information

When you have specific questions or purposes for reading, you should look for **important information** to answer your questions. **Unimportant information** will not suit your specific purpose.

Read the story. Then write the letters of the sentences that are important to each purpose. Each sentence may be used more than once. **Answers may vary.**

   (a) Scientists hope to make a cloth one day that will be as strong as spider silk. **(b)**They may have gotten the idea from an old story. **(c)** The story says that arrows bounced off some soldiers because spider silk was woven into their clothes.
   (d) Spiders make spider silk from their bodies. **(e)** Baby spiders hatch from eggs and then spin a line of silk and wait for the wind to carry them to a new home. **(f)** Tarantulas, who live in holes in the ground, do not make silk.
   (g) People have respect for spiders because of the spiders' skills at building. **(h)** Farmers like them because they eat bugs.
   (i) Spiders spin webs to catch the bugs that they eat. **(j)** Scientists think a giant silk web could capture a plane. **(k)** It could also be used to help hold a bridge in place during an earthquake.

1. **Purpose:** To find out why scientists are interested in spider silk

   a, g, j, k _____

2. **Purpose:** To find out facts about spiders _____d, e, f, h, i_____

3. **Purpose:** To find out other uses for spiders besides for their silk __h__

4. **Purpose:** To find out how spiders have helped people _____c, h_____

5. **Purpose:** To find a story about the use of spider silk _____c_____

At Home: Ask students to underline the important facts in the story.

Antonyms and Synonyms

A **synonym** is a word that has the same, or almost the same, meaning as another word. An **antonym** is a word that has the opposite, or almost opposite, meaning of another word.

Synonyms: *beautiful, pretty*　　　**Antonyms**: *quiet, noisy*

Choose the word from the box that is a synonym for the underlined word in each sentence. Write the word.

turned	covered	gripe	heap	wave

1. May watched the trees <u>sway</u> in the wind. _____**wave**_____

2. All the garden tools were in a <u>pile</u> in the corner. _____**heap**_____

3. Suddenly the rain <u>changed</u> into hail. _____**turned**_____

4. Clouds <u>hid</u> the mountain's peaks. _____**covered**_____

5. It didn't do any good to <u>complain</u> about the cold. _____**gripe**_____

In each group of four words, circle the two words that are either synonyms or antonyms. Write **synonym** if the words are synonyms and **antonym** if the words are antonyms.

6. (rough) (smooth)　take　hide　**antonym**

7. sing　(walk)　(stride)　branch　**synonym**

8. (look)　chase　eat　(stare)　**synonym**

9. (pull)　rush　(push)　sift　**antonym**

10. gray　(clean)　(dirty)　proud　**antonym**

At Home: Have students tell if the following word pairs are synonyms or antonyms: **throw/catch; small/little; soft/hard; rest/nap.**

Context Clues

The words and sentences around a word can help you discover its meaning. **Context clues** can be synonyms, antonyms, or examples. Some sentences even provide an exact definition for a word.

Write a definition for each boldfaced word. **Answers may vary.**

1. It was an **error.** Luckily, we could fix the incorrect word.

   <u>**incorrect**</u>

2. They will **admit** everyone to the play. They will let in children first.

   <u>**let in**</u>

3. Many planets move in wide circles. For example, the earth **revolves** around the sun.

   <u>**move in wide circles**</u>

4. Erin wants to **adopt** a dog and take care of it at her home.

   <u>**take care of it**</u>

5. The afternoon seemed **endless.** The children thought it would go on forever.

   <u>**on forever**</u>

6. The soldier played the **bugle,** a small instrument like a trumpet, every morning and evening.

   <u>**a small instrument like a trumpet**</u>

Unit 2 Vocabulary Review

A. Supply the correct word from the box.

capture	soldiers	darkness	peaks	shelter	halfway

The _____ **soldiers** _____ climbed up the mountain. There

were many high _____ **peaks** _____. They needed to

_____ **capture** _____ the tower on top of the highest peak.

About _____ **halfway** _____ up, they heard a loud bang. They

ran for _____ **shelter** _____ behind a rock. They waited for

night to fall. Then they climbed the rest of the way in

_____ **darkness** _____. They took the army in the tower by

surprise.

B. Label each statement **true** or **false**. If false, explain why.

1. You can pour a liquid. **true** _____

_____

2. Birds hatch eggs. **true** _____

_____

3. You'll get sick if you eat a ripe tomato. **False; when tomatoes are**

ripe, they are ready to eat. _____

4. Echoes don't make any noise. **False; an echo is a kind of sound.**

_____

10 Book 3.1/ Unit 2
Unit 2 Vocabulary Review

At Home: Have students draw a picture to illustrate a
vocabulary word. They can then write a sentence
telling what the picture shows.

73

Unit 2 Vocabulary Review

A. Choose the correct word to write on each line. You need two words for each item.

grains	handful	buffalo	herds	earthquake	area

1. Damon took a _____**handful**_____ of sand. Then he let the _____**grains**_____ fall through his fingers.

2. _____**Buffalo**_____ travel together in _____**herds**_____.

3. An _____**earthquake**_____ is rare in this _____**area**_____ of the country.

B. Supply the correct word from the box.

serious	respect	struggles	schedule

1. Everybody should _____**respect**_____ the judge.

2. Tanya made a _____**serious**_____ mistake.

3. Martha _____**struggles**_____ to stay awake until the end of the show.

4. We need to keep on _____**schedule**_____, or we won't finish at noon.

At Home: Have students write a journal entry about something that is important to them. They should use a vocabulary word in each sentence.

74

Book 3.1/ Unit 2
Unit 2 Vocabulary Review
10

Main Idea

The **main idea** is the major point that an author wants readers to understand. **Supporting details** are small examples and reasons that explain the main idea.

For each main idea below, write some possible supporting details. Answers will vary.

Main Idea: Matt helps out around the house.

Supporting Details:

1. He makes his bed. _____

   _____

2. Matt helps his parents make dinner. _____

   _____

3. Matt and his sister feed the goldfish. _____

   _____

Main Idea: Ashley is a great baseball player.

Supporting Details:

4. Ashley hit three home runs in the last game. _____

   _____

5. She kept the other team from scoring any points. _____

   _____

6. The team voted Ashley captain. _____

   _____

6 Book 3.1/Unit 3
Moses Goes to a Concert

At Home: Have students add one more supporting
detail to each of the main ideas above.

75

Vocabulary

Supply the correct answers. **Answers may vary.**

1. If you wanted to hear music at your party, why would you invite a

    musician? __because he or she can play songs on an instrument__

2. What would you hear at a **concert**? __a musical performance__

    _____

3. After learning how to play the drums, a person might join an **orchestra**.

    What is that? __a group of people who play music together__

    _____

4. What are some musical **instruments**? __piano, drums, guitar, violin,__

    __saxophone__

5. How does a **conductor** help members of a band to play music?

    __by telling them when to start and how fast to play__

6. Why would you stay home from school if you felt **ill**? __to rest and__

    __get better__

At Home: Have students write a story using all the
vocabulary words.

Book 3.1/Unit 3
Moses Goes to a Concert
6

A Special Touch

The *concert* was about to begin. But where was the *conductor*? Oh no! He was *ill*! How would the *orchestra* know what to do?

Each *musician* had a different idea. The violin player thought the orchestra should play without the conductor. The piano player thought she should be the conductor. The horn player thought the musicians should give a speech about each *instrument* they played. The drum player thought they should all go out to lunch.

Then the conductor's wife came in. "I have watched my husband practice. I can do his job," she said.

That night the orchestra gave one of its greatest concerts! Even the local newspapers agreed.

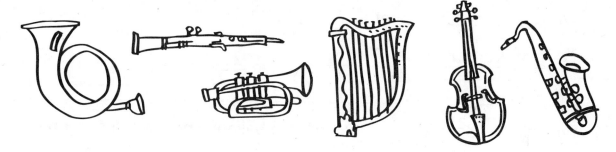

1. What is a person who plays music called?

   a musician

2. What are a violin, a piano, and a horn each called?

   an instrument

3. What is another name for a group of *musicians* playing together?

   an orchestra

4. Who was too ill to be in the concert?

   the conductor

5. How was the orchestra's problem solved?

   The conductor's wife conducted the concert.

 5 Book 3.1/Unit 3
Moses Goes to a Concert

At Home: Ask students how they would have solved the problem faced by the orchestra.

76A

Story Comprehension

Match each character from "Moses Goes to a Concert" with each statement in the right column. Write the letter on the line.

1. Moses __c__

2. Mr. Samuels __d__

3. Ann __b__

4. The percussionist __a__

   a. feels vibrations with her feet.

   b. plays on the marimba.

   c. has a new set of drums.

   d. takes his students to a concert.

Answer the following questions about "Moses Goes to a Concert."

5. Who do the children meet at the concert?

   The children meet Ms. Elwyn.

   _____

6. Why did Mr. Samuels give the children balloons before the concert?

   If they held the balloons, they could feel the vibrations of the

   music.

7. What is a percussionist?

   a musician who plays drums, a huge gong, a marimba, and other

   instruments that are struck

8. What does Moses tell his parents at the end of the story?

   "When you set your mind to it, you can become anything you want

   when you grow up." He says he wants to be a percussionist.

Use a Diagram

Some of the hand positions for letters in American Sign Language look like the written letters. Others use movements that appear to be drawing the letter in the air.

Study these letters. Explain how the fingers are positioned to look like the letter they represent. The first one is done for you.

1.  <u>**The thumb and other four fingers form a C shape.**</u>

2. 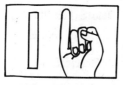 **The pinky is held up alone like an I.**

3.  **The pinky is moved down and up like a J.**

4.  **The thumb and forefinger form an L.**

5.  **The forefinger and middle finger form a V.**

6.  **The forefinger, middle finger, and ring finger form a W.**

7.  **The thumb and pinky form a Y with the arm.**

8.  **The forefinger moves across, down, and across to make a Z.**

8 Book 3.1/Unit 3
Moses Goes to a Concert

At Home: Have students demonstrate the American Sign Language letters shown on this page.

78

Main Idea

To understand a passage better, separate the main idea from the details that support it. The **main idea** is the most important point. **Supporting details** are smaller points that explain the main idea.

Read the following sentences about "Moses Goes to a Concert." Write the main idea of the passage and then write the supporting details. **Answers will vary.**

> Moses has a new set of drums. He likes to play with his new drums, but he can't hear the sound they make. Moses is deaf. He can, however, feel the vibration of his drums with his hands. To feel even more of the vibrations, Moses takes off his shoes. Now he can feel his new drums with his hands and his feet!

Main Idea:

1. Moses can play his drums, even though he is deaf.

_____

Supporting Details:

2. Moses has a new set of drums.

_____

3. Moses plays by feeling the vibrations of the drum through his

hands.

4. Moses has also taken off his shoes,

so he can feel the vibrations

through his feet.

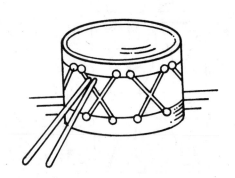

At Home: Have students read a paragraph from an article in a childrens' magazine or newspaper. Then ask them to write down the main idea and supporting details of the paragraph.

Book 3.1/Unit 3
Moses Goes to a Concert 4

Summarize

When you **summarize**, you tell only the most important things that happened. Read each passage below. Then write a summary.
Answers may vary.

1. Last summer, Crystal and her parents drove to Florida. On the way, their car broke down. They worried that they might not make it to Florida. However, they got their car fixed and drove there the next morning.

   Summary: Crystal and her parents had car trouble during their

   drive to Florida.

2. In Florida, they visited Crystal's grandma. Grandma loved to garden. She grew lemon trees, orange trees, and many different types of flowers. She gardened every day.

   Summary: In Florida, they visited Crystal's grandma, who

   loved to garden.

3. Crystal asked Grandma, "Can I work in the garden, too?" Grandma said yes. First, Crystal chose the kind of flowers she wanted. Crystal chose roses. Then, she planted seeds and watered them every day. Grandma said that Crystal's roses would bloom in the spring.

   Summary: Crystal planted roses in Grandma's garden.

4. After two weeks in Florida, it was time to go home. Crystal and her parents hugged Grandma. Crystal felt sad about leaving, but she knew that they would come back in the spring.

   Summary: After two weeks in Florida, Crystal and her parents

   headed home.

4 Book 3.1/Unit 3
Moses Goes to a Concert

At Home: Have students write a one-paragraph summary of the story on this page.

80

Context Clues

When you find an unfamiliar word, read the words and sentences around it. They often can help you figure out the word's meaning.

Look at the underlined word in each example. Circle the words and phrases that help you tell what the word means. Then mark an **X** next to the meaning that fits the underlined word.

1. The musicians walked onto the stage. People clapped and waved.

   The <u>concert</u> was about to begin.

   _____ drums   **X** musical performance   _____ game

2. The singer sang a very high note. She broke a window.

   _____ red   _____ apple pie   **X** sound in music

3. She is a <u>percussionist</u>. She plays the piano, the drums, and many other instruments.

   X type of musician   _____ large van   _____ baby duck

4. Mozart is a famous <u>composer</u>. He wrote many beautiful songs.

   _____ cab driver   _____ dog food   **X** person who creates a musical work

5. He played a pretty <u>melody</u> on the piano. I asked, "What is the name of that song?"

   _____ green   **X** tune   _____ bat

At Home: Have students look up each underlined word in a dictionary to check the meaning.

Book 3.1/Unit 3
Moses Goes to a Concert
10

Story Elements

Understanding the **characters** and the **setting** of a story can help you determine the **plot** of the story.

Read the passage below. Then answer the questions. **Answers will vary.**

Ricardo's art teacher said, "For homework tonight, I would like each of you to paint someone who is special to you." Ricardo decided to paint his cat, Speedy.

That night, Ricardo took out some paint and paper. "Okay, Speedy," he said. "I'm going to paint you. Stand still!" Speedy ran over to Ricardo, jumped on his lap, jumped off his lap, ran into the kitchen, ran into Ricardo's room, pushed a pillow off the bed, and disappeared into the bathroom. "Speedy, stay still!" Ricardo shouted out. "I have to paint you!"

Suddenly the cat appeared again and began to run in circles around Ricardo. Ricardo sat down and thought about what to do next. Suddenly, Ricardo had an idea. "I know—I'll paint Speedy on the go!" he said.

When Ricardo brought his picture to school the next day, everyone liked it. "I'm lucky to have such a fast cat," he said.

1. Who are the main characters in this story? __Ricardo and Speedy__

2. Where does the story take place? __in school and at Ricardo's house__

   _____

3. What is Ricardo's problem? __Speedy won't stand still.__

4. How does Ricardo solve this problem? __He decides to paint Speedy__

   __on the go.__

5. What is the plot of this story? __Ricardo is having a problem finishing__

   __his art homework.__

Book 3.1/Unit 3
**The Little Painter of Sabana
Grande**
5

At Home: Have students write a few sentences explaining why they would or would not like to have Speedy as a pet.

82

Vocabulary

Supply the correct words from the list.

blossoms   dawn   faded   imaginary   miserable   shallow

1. When a flower loses its color, it has _____**faded**_____.

2. A very unhappy person feels _____**miserable**_____.

3. If a pond or lake is not deep, we describe it as _____**shallow**_____.

4. _____**Dawn**_____ is the time of day when the sun first rises.

5. A story that you make up in your mind is _____**imaginary**_____.

6. In spring, many fruit trees produce lovely flowers called ___**blossoms**___.

At Home: Have students look up the vocabulary words in a dictionary and make vocabulary cards for each word to use as a study tool.

Book 3.1/Unit 3
The Little Painter of Sabana Grande

6

Carmen's Garden

One day a mouse named Carmen woke up at *dawn*. She liked to garden early in the morning.

Carmen's garden was behind her house near a stream that was *shallow*. Every day Carmen began by watering seeds she had planted. For weeks she watered and waited. But nothing happened! Waiting made Carmen *miserable*. After weeks of waiting, her hope for pretty flowers had *faded*.

Then one day, she spotted little green stems popping up. She couldn't believe it. "This must be *imaginary*!" she shouted. "The seeds are growing!"

Soon her garden was filled with the *blossoms* of hundreds of flowers.

1. What is the first moment of day called?

   dawn

2. When a stream is not deep, what is it?

   shallow

3. How does waiting make Carmen feel?

   miserable

4. Why does the garden seem *imaginary* to Carmen?

   She had to wait so long for the flowers, she couldn't believe it.

5. Why did Carmen have to wait so long?

   It takes time for flowers to grow.

5
Book 3.1/Unit 3
The Little Painter of Sabana Grande

At Home: Ask students to identify the main idea of the story. Then ask them to point out the supporting details.

83A

Story Comprehension

Think about the story of Fernando, the little painter. Then finish each sentence by writing the missing word on the blank line. Write that word on the crossword puzzle.

ACROSS

1. The smooth and white __adobe__ houses reminded Fernando of paper.

4. Fernando lived in the village of __Sabana__ Grande.

6. Everyone said __kind__ words about Fernando's paintings.

8. The color yellow is made from dried __grasses__ in the meadow.

9. Soon all the neighbors asked Fernando if he would paint their __houses__ .

10. Above the door Fernando painted the words Casa Familia __Espino__ .

DOWN

2. The color __black__ is made from the charcoal of a burned tree stump.

3. Fernando's teacher taught him how the country people of Panama made their __paints__ .

5. The color blue is made from __berries__ that grow deep in the jungle.

7. The __neighbors__ brought out chairs and watched Fernando paint.

At Home: Have students think of two more clues and words to add to the puzzle.

Book 3.1/Unit 3
The Little Painter of Sabana Grande
10

Use a Map

Maps often show more than roads, towns, and the borders of countries. Lines drawn on a map can show many different kinds of information. Sometimes an area on a map is colored or shaded to give information about that area.

Look at this map of a playground. Follow the instructions below to add more information to this map.

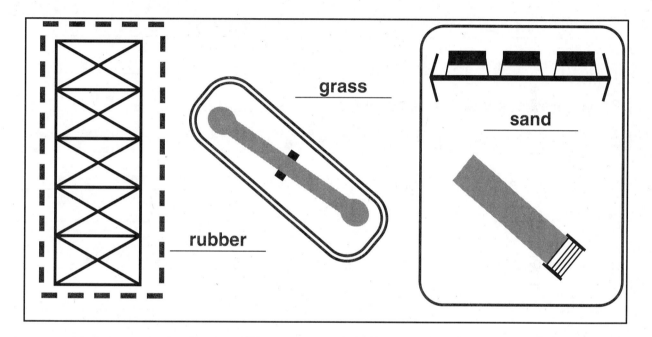

1. Draw a solid line around the swing sets and slides. This area has sand on the ground.

2. Write the word *sand* inside the area marked off by the solid line.

3. Draw a broken line around the gym bars. This area has rubber mats on the ground.

4. Write the word *rubber* next to this area.

5. Draw a double line around the seesaw. This area has grass on the ground.

6. Write the word *grass* next to this area.

Book 3.1/Unit 3
The Little Painter of Sabana Grande

At Home: Ask students to make a map of the playground at their school or in their neighborhood.

85

Story Elements

Choose a word from the list that describes Fernando, and write it on the line. **Answers may vary.**

happy   bored   busy   tired   sad   talented

1. Fernando is _busy._

2. Explain your word choice. **Possible answer: In the story, Fernando is always doing something. He is busy making paint, searching for paper, and painting the outside of his house.**

3. Where does the story take place? **The story takes place in the village of Sabana Grande in Panama.**

4. What is Fernando's problem in the story? **He doesn't have paper to paint on.**

5. How does Fernando solve his problem? **Fernando solves his problem by painting his house.**

6. What do people from the village ask Fernando to do at the end of the story? **People ask Fernando to paint their houses, too.**

At Home: Have students choose a different word from the list to describe Fernando, and explain their choice.

McGraw-Hill School Division

Summarize

Summarize each of the events in the story below. You may want to describe how Bonita feels as well as what she does. **Answers may vary.**

1. **Event 1:** Bonita and her class were writing short stories about their families. Bonita felt excited. She brought in some old family pictures to help give her ideas about her story.

   Bonita looked at family pictures before writing about her family.

   _____

2. **Event 2:** Bonita wrote about her grandfather. Then, Bonita painted a picture of him to go along with her story. Bonita was happy with the way her story was turning out.

   Bonita wrote a story about her grandfather.

   _____

3. **Event 3:** Just then, a gust of wind blew through an open window. Bonita's story flew right out the window. "Now my story is ruined!" Bonita said sadly.

   A gust of wind blew Bonita's story out the window.

   _____

4. **Event 4:** Bonita looked at her family photos. Her grandfather was smiling. Suddenly, Bonita began to smile. "I bet I can write another story about my grandfather," she said. "This one will be even better than the last!"

   Bonita looked at her grandfather's smiling picture and decided to

   write another, even better, story about him.

   _____

Book 3.1/Unit 3
The Little Painter of Sabana Grande
4

At Home: Have students watch a TV show and write a one-paragraph summary of it.

87

Context Clues

When you are reading, you often discover new words. When you come across a puzzling word, look at the words and phrases near it and think about what is happening in the story. These **context clues** often can help you figure out what the word means.

Read each passage. Then use context clues to decide what the underlined word means. Circle the letter next to the correct meaning.

1. She likes to paint <u>landscapes</u>: fields, forests, and ocean shores.

   a. pictures of people

   (b.) pictures of the land

2. Fernando painted <u>blossoms</u> on the wall of his house. The large purple flowers looked as if they were creeping up the wall.

   a. fruits

   (b.) flowers

3. I woke up at <u>dawn</u>. The sky was becoming lighter.

   (a.) the first light that appears in the morning

   b. a math teacher

4. Her art is <u>improving</u>. Each new painting is better than the one before.

   (a.) getting better

   b. feeling sick

5. My class went to see a Chinese art <u>exhibit</u> last week. We saw many beautiful paintings.

   (a.) show

   b. dance

88 At Home: Have students write a short story using some of the words above.

Book 3.1/Unit 3
The Little Painter of Sabana Grande 5

Make Inferences

Sometimes you must **infer**, or figure out, what is happening in a story from clues that the author gives. Read each of the following passages. Then answer each question.

> It was Roxanne's birthday, and she was hoping that someone would give her a book about airplanes. Her Aunt Jackie brought her a present in a box. It was just the right size for a book. Roxanne tore open the package. "I can't wait to find out what is!" she said.

1. How do you think Roxanne felt as she opened up the package?

   excited

2. Which clues helped you make your inference? Roxanne tore open

   the package. She couldn't wait to see what it was.

> Roxanne opened the box and took out a pair of socks. She looked down at them for a minute and sighed very quietly. "Oh . . ." Then she smiled. "Thanks, Aunt Jackie. Just what I needed." Roxanne hugged her aunt.

3. How does Roxanne feel about her present? She feels disappointed.

4. Which clues helped you make your inference? After Roxanne

   opens her present, she says "Oh," and she sighs.

5. How does Roxanne feel about her Aunt Jackie? She likes her and

   doesn't want to hurt her feelings.

6. Which clues helped you make your inference? Roxanne pretends to

   like the present. When she sees the socks, she sighs very

   quietly so that Aunt Jackie won't hear. She smiles, and hugs her.

Vocabulary

gazed   costume   pattern   attic   examined   anxious

Answer the following questions.

1. If you were *anxious* about something, would you be worried or calm?

You would be worried.

2. Would you be more likely to find a *pattern* on flowery wallpaper or in a pile of mud?

on flowery wallpaper

3. If you *gazed* at the sky, would you look at it for a long time or a short time?

for a long time

4. When you are in an *attic* are you in the basement of a house or just under the roof?

just under the roof

5. Would you wear a *costume* while acting in a play or while taking a bath?

while acting in a play

6. If you *examined* something, would you look at it carefully or just glance at it?

carefully

90

At Home: Have students use each of the vocabulary words in a sentence.

Book 3.1/Unit 3
The Patchwork Quilt   6

McGraw-Hill School Division

Guy's Holiday

Guy could not wait for Thanksgiving. He was *anxious* to show his Aunt Cora his Pilgrim *costume*.

When Aunt Cora arrived, she *gazed* at Guy. "My, Pilgrim, how you have grown!" she said.

After dinner, Aunt Cora and Mama told stories of their childhood. Mama went up to the *attic* and brought down a box filled with photos. Guy *examined* each photo.

In one, young Aunt Cora wore a dress with a *pattern* of leaves. It looked just like the dress she had on! "I guess some things never change!" Aunt Cora exclaimed.

After they finished looking at the photographs they ate dessert. This year they had four different kinds of pie.

1. What did Guy wear on Thanksgiving?

   a Pilgrim costume

2. How did Guy feel about showing his costume to his aunt?

   anxious

3. What did Guy's mother get from the *attic*?

   a box of photos

4. What was on Aunt Cora's dress?

   a pattern of leaves

5. Why did Aunt Cora say that some things never change?

   The dress she had on had leaves, like a childhood dress.

5 Book 3.1/Unit 3
   The Patchwork Quilt

At Home: Have students list some of the things they do on Thanksgiving or on another special holiday.

90A

Story Comprehension

Look back over "The Patchwork Quilt." Then complete the chart below. **Answers may vary.**

1. **Setting of story**	Tanya's house
2. **Main characters**	Tanya, Grandma, Mama, Papa, Ted, and Jim
3. **Beginning of story**	Grandma tells Tanya about the patchwork quilt she wants to make. Tanya says that she will help her.
4. **Middle of story**	Grandma gathers patches for her quilt from the family's clothes. Mama decides to help. After Grandma gets sick, the whole family helps cut and prepare patches for the quilt.
5. **End of story**	Grandma feels better and sews the patches of the quilt together.

Now match each patch of clothing or fabric with the person it belonged to in the story.

__b__ 6. gold dress   **a.** Grandma

__a__ 7. piece of old quilt   **b.** Mama

__e__ 8. red shirt   **c.** Tanya

__c__ 9. African princess costume   **d.** Jim

__d__ 10. blue corduroy pants   **e.** Ted

At Home: Have students write a sentence explaining why the patchwork quilt was important to Tanya and her family.

Use a Diagram

A **diagram** can help you see how to put something together. Use these diagrams and directions to create a square from a traditional quilt pattern.

This square is called an Indian Trail. It's also been called Forest Path or Winding Walk. As you can see, it looks like a path winding around and around.

Here are the two sizes of triangles that complete the diagram.

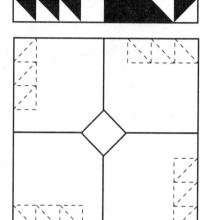

1. Start by drawing four sets of three small triangles. Draw them from each corner as shown at right. Then color them in. Use the dotted outlines as a guide.

2. Add four big triangles to the square as shown. Then color in.

3. Add four sets of three small triangles to the inside of the square as shown.

4. Color in those triangles to complete the quilt.

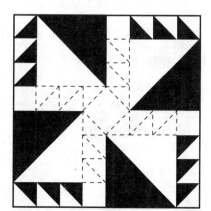

4 Book 3.1/Unit 3
The Patchwork Quilt

At Home: Ask students to make their own simple design for a quilt.

92

Make Inferences

An **inference** is very much like a conclusion. A conclusion is almost certainly true. An inference is probably true.

Read each of the following passages about "The Patchwork Quilt." Then answer each question. **Answers will vary.**

> Grandma's eyes grew distant and dark. She turned away from Tanya and looked out the window for a long time, rubbing the material between her fingers.

1. What do you think Grandma was thinking about? the past and

   the old ways

2. How do you think she felt as she looked out the window?

   sad; longing for the past

3. What information helped you make your inferences? Grandma's

   eyes grew dark, so she was probably feeling sad. Rubbing the

   cloth helped her remember the past.

> Finally, Grandma was ready to do the quilting, but she had one very important thing to add.

4. What "very important thing" did Grandma add to the quilt? She stitched

   "For Tanya from your Mama and Grandma" on one of the patches.

5. When did you learn about the very important thing Grandma wanted to add?

   at the end of the story

6. Why do you think Grandma didn't tell Tanya what she was going to do?

   She wanted to surprise Tanya.

At Home: Have students write a sentence or two explaining whether they think Tanya will teach her children about quiltmaking.

93

Book 3.1/Unit 3
The Patchwork Quilt
6

Main Idea

Read the following paragraphs. Then fill in the details that support the main ideas. **Answers will vary.**

Yesterday, Carl went to the store. His mom and dad are fixing up his room. Carl bought green, brown, and orange paint for the walls and ceiling. Carl asked his mom to order a white shade for the window. For the floor, Carl hopes to find a red rug. Carl's mom thinks that his room will look like a rainbow.

Main Idea: Carl's mom and dad are fixing up his room.

Supporting details:

1. Carl bought paint for the walls and ceiling.

2. Carl asked his mom to order a shade.

3. Carl wants a red rug.

Gina went out to lunch with her friend, Wendy. Both girls had hamburgers. For dessert, Gina had a banana split. Wendy had fresh fruit. After lunch, the two friends went shopping.

Main Idea: Gina went out to lunch with her friend, Wendy.

Supporting details:

1. Both girls had hamburgers.

2. Gina had a banana split for dessert.

3. Wendy had fresh fruit.

At Home: Have students read a short magazine or newspaper article and identify a main idea and two supporting details.

Multiple-Meaning Words

A word with **multiple meanings** has more than one meaning. The words and sentences around a word are called its **context**. Reading the words and sentences around a word can help you choose the correct meaning.

Read each sentence below. Circle the letter of the best meaning of each underlined word. Then, write a new sentence for the underlined word, using the meaning that you did **not** circle. **Sentences will vary.**

1. Tanya's quilt will last a long time.

   a. at the end   **(b.)** stay in good shape

   I came in last in the race.

2. She lost her hat.

   (a.) no longer had   **b.** failed to win

   The baseball team lost the game.

3. I like eating jam and bread.

   (a.) a sweet food made with fruit   **b.** put into a tight space

   She tried to jam all her papers into her desk.

4. I stood in line at the store.

   a. a long, thin mark   **(b.)** people standing one after the other

   I drew a line on the paper.

At Home: Have students underline the context clue that helped them to define the underlined word in each sentence.

Book 3.1/Unit 3
The Patchwork Quilt

8

Story Elements

Understanding the main **characters** and the **setting** can help you understand what happens in a story.

Read the story below. Then answer the questions.

Today in class, everyone was supposed to write a story. Jamar couldn't think of anything to write about, so he asked his friends for some ideas.

Erica said, "Write about horses."

Pedro said, "Write about a ship."

Bill suggested, "Write about a doctor."

He raised his hand. "Mr. Diaz, what should I do?" he said. "I'll never think of a story. I asked all my friends, but I don't want to write about the things they suggested."

Mr. Diaz said, "Usually, it's a good idea to write about things you like."

Jamar thought about it. "I like baseball. I know! I'll write a story about a baseball player who becomes an all-star!"

1. Where does the story take place? The story takes place in class.

_____

2. Who is the main character? Jamar is the main character.

_____

3. What is Jamar's problem? He can't think of anything to write about.

_____

4. What does Jamar decide to do at the end of the story?

He decides to write about something he likes—baseball.

_____

_____

4 | Book 3.1/Unit 3
Pecos Bill:
A Tall Tale Play

At Home: Have students write a few sentences explaining how Jamar tries to solve his problem.

96

Vocabulary

Write the vocabulary word that best fits in each of the sentences below.

combine   invented   located   prairie   stumbled   wilderness

1. Let's _____**combine**_____ your hard work with my good ideas.

   By joining together, we can do a much better job.

2. The scientist was well-known for thinking of useful new things. He

   _____**invented**_____ egg timers and staplers, and he even made

   the first nonstick pan!

3. I live on Fire Street between the courthouse and the library. Where is

   your house _____**located**_____?

4. I was camping in the forest. Crickets were singing, and frogs were

   croaking. It was so lovely being out there in the _____**wilderness**_____.

5. The flat, grassy fields seemed like they would never end, and I hadn't

   seen a tree for miles. "This has to be the biggest _____**prairie**_____

   in the United States," I thought to myself.

6. My brother stepped on his shoelace, _____**stumbled**_____, and then

   cried out as he fell down.

At Home: Have students think of other words that mean almost the same thing as the vocabulary words. Then have them use these words as clues for a vocabulary puzzle, crossword puzzle, or game.

Book 3.1/Unit 3
Pecos Bill:
A Tall Tale Play
6

Save the Animals!

Jed left his home on the *prairie*. He hoped to reach the edge of the *wilderness* before the sun set. He had something important to do.

Jed had *invented* a way to protect animals from floods. He wanted to show his invention to some of the animals along the way. The problem was, he couldn't find any animals! By late afternoon, Jed was about to give up. Suddenly he *stumbled* across a fox and her young. "Get away!" the fox shouted. "You will not hurt my babies and me!"

"I am here to help you," said Jed. "Let's *combine* what we know to save the animals. You tell me where the other animals are *located,* and I will share my invention with them."

The fox thought about it for a moment. Then she agreed. "I will show you," she said. "Follow me!"

1. Who *stumbled* across a fox?

    Jed
    _____

2. Where was Jed's home?

    on the prairie
    _____

3. What had Jed *invented*?

    a way to protect animals from floods
    _____

4. Where was Jed walking?

    to the edge of the wilderness
    _____

5. Why did Jed want to get to the animals?

    to share his invention
    _____

 5

Book 3.1/Unit 3
Pecos Bill:
A Tall Tale Play

At Home: Encourage students to think of ways that animals might be protected from hunters.

97A

Story Comprehension

In "Pecos Bill," Cowboy Sam and Cowgirl Pam tell a story to Cookie and the ranch hands. "Pecos Bill" is a story within a story. Fill in the chart for each story.

	Main Story	Story Within a Story
Setting	cowboy camp in Texas	Texas
Characters	Cowboy Sam, Cowgirl Pam, Cookie, and the ranch hands	Pa, Ma, Pecos Bill, the other children, coyotes, Carl the Cowboy, Slue-Foot Sue, and the Judge
Beginning	They order pizza. Sam and Pam start telling a story.	Bill's family decides to go west.
Middle	The pizza comes.	Baby Bill falls out of the wagon. Coyotes raise him. Years later, Carl the Cowboy finds Bill and teaches him how to be a cowboy. Bill invents different things.
End	Everyone goes to sleep.	Bill meets and marries Slue-Foot Sue.

At Home: Ask students to circle the part of the chart that represents the plot.

Use a Map

Use the map to answer the questions.

1. Some farmers asked Paul and Babe to clear land for farming. In one day, with a few swings of his huge ax, Paul removed every tree in two states. In which two states did he do this?

   <u>**North Dakota, South Dakota**</u>

2. Paul Bunyan took a shovel and dug out Puget Sound on the West Coast. In which state did this take place? <u>**Washington**</u>

3. Babe needed new shoes. Paul needed a lot of iron to make four shoes Babe's size. Paul had to dig out three huge brand new iron mines. In which Midwestern state did he do this? <u>**Minnesota**</u>

4. When Babe was thirsty, Paul decided to dig out Lake Michigan so he could have a water bowl his own size. Between which two states is Lake Michigan? <u>**Wisconsin and Michigan**</u>

4 / Book 3.1/Unit 3
Pecos Bill:
A Tall Tale Play

At Home: Ask students to name the states on the map not mentioned in the questions above.

99

Story Elements

Understanding what the **characters** in a story do as well as where they do it helps us to understand what the story is about.

Answer the following questions.

1. Where are Cookie, Cowgirl Pam, Cowboy Sam, and the cowhands?

   They are sitting around a fire in a cowboy camp in the Southwest.

   _____

2. Why do Sam and Pam have time to tell the story of Pecos Bill?

   They have time because they are waiting for pizza to be delivered.

   _____

3. Why was Bill's family always moving?

   The family was always moving because Bill's father didn't like

   living near other people.

4. How did Pecos Bill get his name?

   He fell off of his parents' wagon while they were crossing the

   Pecos River.

5. How did Bill invent the lasso?

   He grabbed a rattlesnake and used it to rope a steer.

   _____

6. How did Pecos Bill first meet Slue-Foot Sue?

   He saw her riding a catfish, and Cowboy Carl introduced him to

   her.

At Home: Have students organize their answers in a three-column chart. Have them label the columns as follows: Character, Setting, Plot.

100

Book 3.1/Unit 3
Pecos Bill:
A Tall Tale Play   6

Make Inferences

Sometimes a character in a story doesn't say exactly how he or she feels about something. Readers must then **infer** how the character feels by thinking about what the character says or does, or how he or she acts.

Read the sentences below. Then, in the right column, write down how the character feels.

What Character Says or Does	How Character Feels
1. "No, I am not mad!" Michael yelled, angrily waving his fists in the air.	Michael feels angry.
2. "Kate!" Samantha shouted. "I can't believe you're finally here!" She hugged her friend tightly.	Samantha feels happy to see her friend.
3. Vera said, "We should try to stay calm." Her knees were shaking and her teeth were chattering.	Vera feels scared.
4. Shane had to make lunch for himself. Then he had to clean his room. After that, he had to finish his homework. He sat down at the table with a loud groan and closed his eyes.	Shane isn't happy about having so much to do.

Book 3.1/Unit 3
Pecos Bill:
A Tall Tale Play
4

At Home: Ask students to explain an instance in their own lives when they had to make an inference.

101

Multiple-Meaning Words

A **multiple-meaning** word has more than one meaning.

Read each sentence below. Then, match each sentence with the correct definition of the underlined word. Write the letter of the answer on the line.

__a__ **1.** I am a big baseball fan.

__i__ **2.** There is a fly in my soup.

__h__ **3.** She tried to fix the broken table.

__e__ **4.** A duck is a kind of bird.

__c__ **5.** Did you see the school play? He had a big part in it.

__b__ **6.** You are very kind.

__g__ **7.** We put on the fan because it was hot.

__f__ **8.** Birds can fly high.

__d__ **9.** Lucy was in a big fix.

__j__ **10.** Let's play ball!

a. a person who is very excited about something

b. nice

c. a story that is acted out on stage

d. trouble

e. a type

f. to move through the air with wings

g. a machine that moves the air

h. to repair

i. type of insect

j. to do something for fun

102

At Home: Have students look through the dictionary to find new multiple-meaning words.

Book 3.1/Unit 3
Pecos Bill: A Tall Tale Play
10

Main Idea

In a passage, the **main idea** is the most important point. **Supporting details** explain the main idea. Read the following story. Then write down the main idea and the supporting details.

Winter is my favorite time of year. In winter, I spend my days playing outside in the cold. I love to build people out of snow. I also love to ice skate. At the end of each day, I love to come out of the cold and drink hot chocolate.

Main Idea:

1. Winter is my favorite time of year._____

_____

Supporting Details:

2. I love to build people out of snow._____

_____

3. I love to ice skate._____

_____

4. I love to drink hot chocolate._____

_____

At Home: Have students think of a main idea for a story and three supporting details. Encourage them to write a story using this informantion.

Vocabulary

Write the vocabulary word that fits in each of the sentences below.

beauty   creeps   furniture   palace   pure   visitors

1. The cat _____**creeps**_____ quietly toward the old sock. Does the cat think the sock is a mouse?

2. Everyone was surprised when the king and queen sold the royal _____**palace**_____. A week after that, they moved into a two-bedroom apartment.

3. My next-door neighbor had many friends. She always welcomed _____**visitors**_____ into her home.

4. Mary bought the brown table. She thought it would look good with her other _____**furniture**_____.

5. This water is very clean and _____**pure**_____. It comes from a spring in the mountains.

6. The ugly duckling did not know that one day it would be a bird of great _____**beauty**_____.

Chills and Thrills

Some people are not happy when winter comes. They do not like the way the cold *creeps* into their clothes. Eli, however, thinks winter is *pure* joy. He loves the *beauty* of the ice on the trees. He loves the limbs of the trees without their leaves.

Eli liked making a snow *palace* out of ice and snow. One day, he tried to bring a chair into his palace. The room needed *furniture*. It also needed some *visitors*. But neither things nor people fit in Eli's tiny snow cave.

Eli didn't mind too much. His dog could fit in the cave. And with that white fur, she looked like a big, warm polar bear! Eli's dog loved winter as much as Eli did.

1. How does the cold get into people's clothes?

   It creeps.

2. What kind of *furniture* did Eli try to bring to his cave?

   a chair

3. Who could not fit in Eli's cave?

   people

4. Which *visitor* could fit into Eli's cave?

   his dog

5. How does Eli feel about the winter time?

   It gives him pure joy because it is beautiful and he can build

   snow caves.

---

5 Book 3.1/Unit 3
A Very Cool Place to Visit

At Home: Have students discuss the different things they do in each of the four seasons. Then have them draw a picture showing one of the activities for each season.

(104A)

Story Comprehension

Answer the following questions about "A Very Cool Place to Visit."

1. What parts of the hotel are made out of ice and snow? <u>The building</u>

   <u>and some of the furniture are made out of ice and snow.</u>

   _____

2. Why do people want to stay at the hotel? <u>People want to stay</u>

   <u>there because it's beautiful and quiet.</u>

   _____

3. Name two ways that guests stay warm at the Ice Hotel.

   <u>Answers may vary. Guests use extra-warm clothes and sleeping</u>

   <u>bags; they exercise before going to bed; they cover their beds</u>

   <u>with skins.</u>

   _____

4. What greets visitors as they arrive at the hotel? <u>A reindeer greets</u>

   <u>guests.</u>

5. What happens each spring? <u>The hotel melts.</u>

   _____

At Home: Have students imagine that they are visiting the Ice Hotel for a night, and have them write about their experiences.

105

Book 3.1/Unit 3
A Very Cool Place to Visit 5

Use a Map

The map of Finland below is divided into four districts: the Upland District, the Lake District, the Coastal Lowlands, and the Coastal Islands.

Write the name of the district beside the description of it.

1. This district contains many lakes. Forests cover most of the land.

   Lake District

2. This district is found in the far north. It has the smallest population.

   Upland District

3. This district contains many small islands off the coast. Many Finns
   have summer cottages there. **Coastal Islands**

4. This district is found along the Gulf of Bothnia and the Gulf of Finland.
   Most of the farms and a milder climate can be found there.

   Coastal Lowlands

5. In which district can the capital, Helsinki, be found?

   Coastal Lowlands

5   Book 3.1/Unit 3
A Very Cool Place to Visit

At Home: Ask students to name the country that
borders Finland to its west.

106

Summarize

A **summary** tells the main ideas of a story.

Read the paragraphs about "A Very Cool Place to Visit." Then summarize each paragraph in one sentence.

1. At one place in Sweden, the cold is everywhere. Guests feel it in their toes, fingers, and noses. Welcome to the Ice Hotel, where the building and even some of the furniture are made of snow and ice.

   It is very cold at the Ice Hotel. _____

   _____

2. Why would people want to stay in a hotel that was cold and frozen? A worker at the hotel, says people love the hotel for its beauty. "The white fresh snow is pure winter." She also says that people want to see the northern lights.

   People stay at the hotel because it is beautiful. _____

   _____

3. Before you get into bed, you have to warm yourself up. Doing some push-ups at bedtime will help you feel warm even before you get into bed!

   Guests exercise to warm themselves up before bed. _____

   _____

4. In the springtime, when the weather gets warmer, the hotel melts. When winter returns, a new building is built from fresh snow and ice. And once again, the Ice Hotel welcomes everyone into its cold and wintry world.

   Every year, the hotel melts and a new hotel is built. _____

   _____

At Home: Have students summarize "A Very Cool Place to Visit."

107

Book 3.1/Unit 3
A Very Cool Place to Visit 4

Multiple-Meaning Words

A word with **multiple meanings** has more than one meaning. Reading the words and sentences around a word can help you choose the correct meaning.

This list has two meanings for each underlined word in the sentences below. Look at the way each underlined word is used in the sentence. Then choose the right meaning for each word from the list.

between winter and summer	<u>or</u>	leap
not warm	<u>or</u>	sickness
move in a secret way	<u>or</u>	a dishonest person
pieces of something hard	<u>or</u>	gets in the way

1. At one hotel in Sweden, the cold doesn't have to <u>sneak</u> in.

   <u>move in a secret way</u>

2. The hotel's 100 beds are made from ice <u>blocks</u> covered with reindeer skins. <u>pieces of something hard</u>

3. Each <u>spring</u>, when the weather warms up, the hotel melts.

   <u>between winter and summer</u>

4. Once again, the Ice Hotel is ready to welcome people into the <u>cold</u>.

   <u>not warm</u>

Context Clues

Context clues are words before or after an unfamiliar word that help us to understand its meaning.

Circle the context clues in each sentence that help you to figure out the meaning of the word in dark type. Then write a possible definition for the word. **Answers may vary.**

1. (Nothing grew) from this **barren** land.

   barren: **where nothing grows** _____

2. The girls ate the **entire** pie, and (there wasn't even a crumb left.)

   entire: **the whole thing** _____

3. He **improved** the garden when he (made better) paths through the roses.

   improved: **made better** _____

4. Grandma tells many (tales) and **legends** about our ancestors.

   legends: **tales** _____

5. The (angry) **scowl** (on your face makes you look very unhappy.)

   scowl: **an angry expression** _____

6. The **antique** clock was (from a time long ago.)

   antique: **very old, from another time** _____

At Home: Ask students to compare their definitions
with the ones in the dictionary.

109

Book 3.1/Unit 3
A Very Cool Place to Visit

6

Unit 3 Vocabulary Review

A. Supply the correct word from the box.

orchestra	concert	imaginary	conductor	musician

Helen pretended she was the _____conductor_____ of an

_____orchestra_____ . She could hear the _____imaginary_____

music in her head. When she waved her arms, each

_____musician_____ played faster. The pretend audience

clapped wildly. At the end of the _____concert_____ , they

threw her flowers.

B. Read each word in Column 1. Then find a word in Column 2 that
means the opposite. Write the letter of the word on the line.

1. shallow __c__   **a.** bright

2. ill __e__   **b.** cellar

3. miserable __f__   **c.** deep

4. faded __a__   **d.** lost

5. attic __b__   **e.** well

6. stumbled __g__   **f.** happy

7. located __d__   **g.** leaped

12 Book 3.1/Unit 3
Unit 3 Vocabulary Review   **At Home:** Have students write a story that uses the
vocabulary words in Part B.   **110**

Unit 3 Vocabulary Review

A. Answer the questions. Then explain each answer by writing what the vocabulary word means.

1. Which is more likely to have a pattern on it, a star or a sweater?

   A sweater; pattern means "a design made of colors, shapes,

   or lines."

2. Would you find blossoms on a tree or on a bird? **A tree; blossoms**

   are flowers.

3. What would you do at dawn, wake up or eat lunch? **Wake up; dawn**

   means "first light of morning."

4. Which would you combine, a fried egg and milk or bread and butter?

   Bread and butter; combine means "to put together."

5. Which would you find in the wilderness, a deer or a grocery store?

   A deer; wilderness means "a place where no people live."

B. Label each column with a word from the box below.

costume	furniture	instrument

furniture	costume	instrument
bed	sailor	piano
chair	scarecrow	horn
table	magician	drum

At Home: Have students make lists like the ones in Part B that name things you could find in the wilderness.

Book 3.1/Unit 3
Unit 3 Vocabulary Review 8

Sequence of Events

In a story, events take place in a certain order, or **sequence.**

Read the two sets of events below. They are out of order.
Number each event in its proper order.

Set A

__5__ Luis got back up and said, "Dad, I hurt my knee."

__4__ "Ouch," Luis yelled, and tried to get back up.

__3__ Luis fell down and hurt his knee.

__2__ Luis tripped over a rock.

__1__ Luis and his father went outside for a walk.

Set B

__5__ Luis's knee felt better.

__2__ Luis's father said, "I think it's just a scratch. Let's go home and take care of it."

__1__ Luis's father came up to him and looked at his knee.

__4__ Luis's father put a bandage on his knee.

__3__ Luis and his father carefully washed the knee with soap and water.

10 Book 3.2/Unit 1
    The Terrible EEK

At Home: Have students list the sequence of events
from a recent newspaper story or television show.

112

Vocabulary

Answer **true** or **false** to each statement. Explain the false statements.

1. When you have *completely* finished your chores, it means that you have nothing left to do. _____ True _____

2. Dogs, cats, and elephants are good examples of *humans*. __False; only__ __people are called humans.__

3. Breakfast, lunch, and dinner are different *meals* that we eat during the day. _____ True _____

4. When a car is moving, it is in *motion*. _____ True _____

5. An answer to a question is known as a *reply*. _____ True _____

6. To find out someone's *weight*, you need a measuring tape. __False;__ __you need a scale.__

At Home: Have students write a paragraph describing their favorite meal.

Book 3.2/Unit 1
The Terrible EEK 6

THE WORLD OF YES

At night it is usually *completely* dark. You can barely see anything. That is, unless there is a full moon.

Most *humans* are asleep during the night. But many animals spend the night in a constant state of *motion*. This is feeding time, the time for munching and crunching.

Some animals are known to eat more than their own *weight* in food— each and every night! What would you say if someone asked whether or not you could do the same thing? "Impossible!" you'd probably *reply*. "That is too big a *meal* for me!"

For the many animals that feed at night, the more snacks they find, the better sleep they'll have ... during the day!

1. What is another way of saying *answer*?

   reply

2. What is another word for *people*?

   humans

3. Being "on the go" means being in what kind of state?

   motion

4. At night some animals eat this.

   a meal

5. Why do you think some animals feed at night?

   Possible answers: It is cooler; it is less dangerous.

---

5   Book 3.2/Unit 1
    The Terrible EEK

At Home: Ask students what types of animals might forage for food at night.

(113A)

Story Comprehension

Think about what happens in "The Terrible EEK"
Then complete the summary below.

Beginning

One rainy night in **(1)** _____the mountains_____ long ago, a father

tells his son that he is most afraid of **(2)** _____a terrible leak_____.

A **(3)** ___thief___ thinks he hears a "terrible eek." A **(4)** _____wolf_____

doesn't know what a terrible leak is. Both the thief and the wolf think the

father is talking about **(5)** _____a scary creature_____. When the thief falls

on the wolf, both are **(6)** _____frightened_____. Each of them thinks **(7)**

_____the other one_____ is the "terrible eek."

Middle

After the thief **(8)** _____falls into a hole_____, the wolf returns to

(9) _____his den_____. The wolf asks the tiger **(10)** ___to help him catch___

_____the "terrible leak"_____. They go to **(11)** ___the hole___

where the thief fell. A monkey goes too.

End

The monkey pulls **(12)** _____the thief_____ out of the hole

with his tail. By now, they all are so frightened that **(13)** ___they scream___

___and run away___ Meanwhile, the boy and his father are **(14)** ___sound___

___asleep___ in their beds.

At Home: Have students underline the setting and
circle the characters in their summaries.

Use a Chart

A **chart** arranges facts and figures in an easy-to-read layout. Fill in the chart by using the information in the sentences below.

1. At Mountain School, they had 56 days of rainfall.

2. At Valley School, they had 67 inches of snow.

3. At Coastal School, they measured 85 inches of rain.

4. At Inland School, they had only 2 total days of snowfall.

5. The smallest amount of snow was 8 inches and it fell at the Inland School.

Reported Rainfall and Snowfall At Area Grade Schools in One Year

School	Rain (in inches)	Snow (in inches)	Total Days of Rainfall	Total Days of Snowfall
Mountain School	21	120	56	39
Valley School	11	67	43	33
Coastal School	85	12	101	4
Inland School	4	8	21	2

Sequence of Events

In a story, events take place in a certain **sequence**, or order.

Read the events below from "The Terrible EEK" The events are listed out of order. Write the events in order.

The thief landed on the back of the wolf.
The wolf ran into the woods.
"Father, are you ever afraid?" the boy asked.
The thief grabbed a branch.
The thief fell into a hole.
The wolf asked the tiger for help.
The father told the boy that he was most afraid of a terrible leak.
The branch broke.

1. "Father, are you ever afraid?" the boy asked.

2. The father told the boy that he was most afraid of a terrible leak.

3. The thief landed on the back of the wolf.

4. The wolf ran into the woods.

5. The thief grabbed a branch.

6. The branch broke.

7. The thief fell into a hole.

8. The wolf asked the tiger for help.

At Home: Have students write two more story events in the proper places on their lists.

Book 3.2/Unit 1
The Terrible EEK   8

Form Generalizations

A generalization is a broad statement that is based on examples.

Think of some things you have heard about animals. Write a generalization about each animal. **Answers may vary.**

1. dog

  Dogs chase cats.

2. cat

  Cats chase mice.

3. mouse

  Mice like cheese.

4. parrot

  Parrots can learn to talk.

5. elephant

  Elephants never forget.

6. cricket

  Crickets chirp loudly in the summer.

Suffixes

A **suffix** is a word part that can be added to the end of a word. Adding a suffix creates a new word with its own meaning. Sometimes the spelling of the base word changes when a suffix is added. Some common suffixes include:

-y ("full of" or "having")   **-ly** ("in a certain manner")

In each of the following sentences, circle the suffix in the underlined word. Then write a new sentence, replacing the underlined word with a phrase that has the same meaning. For example, replace the underlined word sunny with the phrase *full of sun*.

1. She smiled sweet(ly) at me.

   She smiled at me in a sweet manner.

2. He speaks very quiet(ly).

   He speaks in a very quiet manner.

3. Yesterday it was rain(y).

   Yesterday it was full of rain .

4. I wish the sky were not so cloud(y).

   I wish the sky were not so full of clouds.

5. The children smiled happi(ly) at one another.

   The children smiled at one another in a happy manner.

6. He looked at me strange(ly).

   He looked at me in a strange manner.

At Home: Have students write two lists of words. One should have words that end with -ly; the other should have words that end with -y.

118

Book 3.2/Unit 1
The Terrible EEK

12

Author's Purpose, Point of View

Here are three common purposes or reasons why authors write: to **inform**, or to give readers facts; to **persuade**, or to convince readers to believe or do something; to **entertain**, or to tell a good story.

Read each passage. On the first line following each passage, write one of the three purposes described in bold type above to explain why the author wrote the passage. On the second line, write the author's **point of view**, the way he or she feels about the story.

Art class should be an hour long, not half an hour. Right now, we never have enough time to finish our work. If art class were longer, we would work better and learn more. Art is a very important class. We should take it seriously.

1. Purpose: _____ **to persuade**

2. Point of view: _____ **Author cares about learning art.**

I love knock-knock jokes. Listen to this one: "Knock, knock!" "Who's there?" "Boo." "Boo who?" "Why are you crying?"

3. Purpose: _____ **to entertain**

4. Point of view: _____ **Knock-knock jokes are funny.**

There are five different schools in my town. About 500 students go to each school. There are three grade schools, one junior high school, and one high school. This year I still go to grade school. Next year I will go to junior high school. I can't wait!

5. Purpose: _____ **to inform**

6. Point of view: _____ **Author feels excited about going to junior high school.**

At Home: Have students add a few sentences to one of the passages above, keeping the same purpose.

Vocabulary

Supply the correct words from the list. The same vocabulary word is used twice in each example.

members	dozens	comforting
relatives	encouraging	designed

1. We had to bake _____dozens_____ of cookies to feed everyone who came to the meeting. A dozen is a group of twelve. The word _____dozens_____ is used to describe large numbers of things.

2. My piano teacher kept _____encouraging_____ me to practice until I finally learned the new song. If you are _____encouraging_____ people, you are giving them hope and the courage to get things done.

3. Last week, our club welcomed seven new _____members_____. People who belong to a group such as a team or a family are known as _____members_____.

4. During the holidays my grandparents and a few other _____relatives_____ come for dinner. _____Relatives_____ are people in the same family.

5. The nurse was feeding and _____comforting_____ her patients to help them get well. _____Comforting_____ people means trying to make them feel better.

6. Jack's sister _____designed_____ a new coat for herself. When something is _____designed_____, it is planned, drawn, or outlined.

At Home: Have students design an article of clothing that they would like to wear. They can draw a picture, or they can cut out a design on colored paper.

Book 3.2/Unit 1
In My Family 12

Happy, Happy Birthday!

The Fourth of July is a special day at Jake's house. All of his *relatives* come to visit. The *members* of Jake's family have a great big birthday party for two. It is Jake's birthday and the birthday of the United States.

At the party, Jake's father cooks *dozens* of hamburgers on a grill. There is always someone next to the grill *encouraging* him to make more.

Dessert is always fun. Everyone eats the birthday cake that Jake's mother has *designed*. It has a red, white, and blue flag.

Jake finds it *comforting* that he and his country have the same birthday. He will always have a special friend on his special day—the United States!

1. What were people *encouraging* Jake's father to do?

   <u>**make more hamburgers**</u>

2. What is another name for cousins, aunts, uncles, and grandparents?

   <u>**relatives**</u>

3. Who *designed* the cake?

   <u>**Jake's mother**</u>

4. What does Jake find *comforting*?

   <u>**His birthday is the same as the United States' birthday.**</u>

5. Who were celebrating together in the story?

   <u>**The members of Jake's family.**</u>

5 | Book 3.2/Unit 1
In My Family

At Home: Have students design on paper cakes to celebrate a holiday of their choice.

120A

Story Comprehension

Answer these questions about "In My Family."

1. Why would the mother and grandmother be angry with the children?

   The mother and grandmother would be angry with the children for

   playing in the hot sun in the middle of the day.

2. What did Arturo try to feed to the toad?

   Arturo tried to feed an ant to the toad.

3. What is the grandfather's name?

   The grandfather's name is Antonio Lomas.

4. Who is watching the grandfather work?

   Margie is watching the grandfather work.

5. Why is there no place to sit in Aunt Paz and Uncle Beto's house?

   There is no place to sit because there are plates of empanadas

   everywhere.

6. Who made Mary Jane's birthday cake?

   Mary Jane's mother made the birthday cake.

7. Where do people dance in the summer?

   People dance outside.

8. Who taught Carmen how to dance?

   Carmen's father and grandfather taught her how to dance.

McGraw-Hill School Division

Use a Diagram

Fill in the blanks in the diagram with the name or dates for the underlined family member.

1. The life span of <u>Dorothy Ray</u> was 1895–1966.

2. Lester Mills is a child of <u>George Mills</u>.

3. Cathy Moss married <u>Oliver Mills</u>.

4. Vicky is one of <u>Sara Mills</u> and <u>Paul Wilson</u>'s three children.

5. Emma Penn married <u>Kevin Mills</u>.

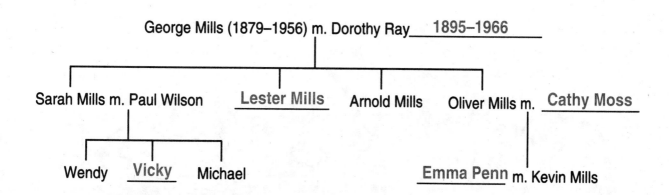

George Mills (1879–1956) m. Dorothy Ray____1895–1966____

Sarah Mills m. Paul Wilson   <u>Lester Mills</u>   Arnold Mills   Oliver Mills m. Cathy Moss

Wendy   Vicky   Michael

<u>Emma Penn</u> m. Kevin Mills

5 | Book 3.2/Unit 1
In My Family

At Home: Have students try to write a family tree
diagram for their family.

122

Author's Purpose, Point of View

Sometimes an author has more than one purpose in telling a story. What purposes do you think the author had for writing "In My Family"? Answer each question below. **Answers may vary.**

Did you enjoy the story? Tell two things about the story that entertained you.

1. <u>I enjoyed the description of the toads.</u>

2. <u>I enjoyed the description of the dancing</u>

What did you learn as you read the story? Tell three things that you learned by reading "In My Family."

3. <u>I learned what horned toads are.</u>

4. <u>I learned how to cook some Spanish foods.</u>

5. <u>I learned some Spanish words.</u>

What do you think is the author's point of view about her family?

6. **She feels very close to members of her family. She enjoys being**

   part of her family.

At Home: Have students write a paragraph that informs the reader. The paragraph may be about their family, if they wish.

Book 3.2/Unit 1
In My Family
6

Sequence of Events

Events in a story happen in a certain **sequence**, or order.

Read the events below. They are out of order. Use the boxes to draw the events in order.

Mary's mother said, "Thank you," and gave her a hug.

Mary gave the card to her mother.

Mary drew balloons on the card and wrote, "Happy Mother's Day, Mom!"

Mary got paper, crayons, and a card.

1. **Mary got paper and crayons.**	2. **Mary made a Mother's Day card.**
3. **Mary gave the card to her mother.**	4. **Mary's mother said, "Thank you," and gave her a hug.**

Figurative Language

Have you ever heard someone say, "It's raining cats and dogs"? Of course, cats and dogs aren't really falling from the sky. But this exaggeration gets across the idea of heavy rain in a colorful way. Imaginative phrases such as this are called **figurative language.**

A **simile** is a type of figurative language that makes a comparison using the word **like** or **as**. The following sentence is an example of a simile. He was as tall as a giant.

Read each pair of sentences. Write **S** next to the one that is an example of a simile.

1. _____ I like to draw the lake.

   __S__ The lake is as shiny as a piece of glass.

2. __S__ The chair was as hard as a rock.

   _____ The chair was too small for me.

3. _____ Carmen has fun looking at the toads.

   __S__ Carmen is as free of cares as a toad.

4. __S__ His hands felt as cold as ice.

   _____ He put his hands in his pockets.

5. __S__ He is as quiet as a mouse.

   _____ He never talks to anyone.

6. __S__ The cat was as round as a ball.

   _____ The cat was small and round.

At Home: Ask students to circle the figurative language in each sentence they chose.

Cause and Effect

A **cause** is the reason something happened. An **effect** is what happened.

Read each pair of sentences below.
Write *cause* next to each sentence that explains why something happened.
Write *effect* next to those that tell what happened.

1. Max was afraid. _____cause_____

2. Max screamed. _____effect_____

3. Terence ate dinner. _____effect_____

4. Terence felt hungry. _____cause_____

5. Everything was covered in snow. _____effect_____

6. Snow fell all night. _____cause_____

7. Otto had a cold. _____cause_____

8. Otto stayed home from school. _____effect_____

9. Gregory woke up late. _____cause_____

10. Gregory was late to school. _____effect_____

11. Mary studied hard. _____cause_____

12. Mary did well on the test. _____effect_____

12 Book 3.2/Unit 1
Cactus Hotel

At Home: Have students write one more pair of
sentences showing cause and effect.

126

Vocabulary

Complete each sentence with a word from the list below.

discovered	insects	remains
ribs	tough	treat

1. Birds like to eat tiny _____insects_____ that live on leaves.

2. You could find the _____remains_____, or what is left behind, of a fallen cactus lying on the desert floor.

3. Wooden _____ribs_____, like the bony ones in your chest, hold up a giant cactus from the inside.

4. The walls of a woodpecker's home inside a cactus are _____tough_____ not weak.

5. Nectar is a delicious _____treat_____ that a bird might find in a cactus flower.

6. An owl _____discovered_____, or found, an empty hole in a cactus and decided to live there.

HOME SWEET HOME

At Home: Have students write a new sentence for each of the vocabulary words.

Treasures on the Beach

It was Sunday. There was no school and I was walking on the beach. The birds were so far away they looked like tiny *insects*.

As I walked I *discovered* the *remains* of an old ship. Most of it had washed away. But some of its wooden *ribs* were still sticking out of the sand. The wood looked smooth and *tough*.

Inside the ship was a treasure chest. Inside the great box were many beautiful things. There were beautiful clothes and lots of jewelry. One thing really caught my eye. It was a big shining ring. What a *treat*!

Then, just as I was about to put on the ring, a bird swooped down and grabbed it! Oh well. At least I had a nice walk on the beach.

1. What was *discovered* by the speaker?

   <u>**the remains of a ship**</u>

2. What was the *treat* that was found?

   <u>**the big ring**</u>

3. What words describe the ship's wooden *ribs*?

   <u>**tough and smooth**</u>

4. What did the birds in the sky look like?

   <u>**insects**</u>

5. Why was the speaker not very upset about losing the ring?

   <u>**She or he still had a nice walk on the beach.**</u>

5 Book 3.2/Unit 1
Cactus Hotel

At Home: Ask the students how their *ribs* are like the ribs of the ship in the story. How are they different?

127A

Story Comprehension

The saguaro cactus has a very long life!

Add details from "Cactus Hotel." Tell what the cactus looks like and what animals are found on or near the cactus at each stage of its growth. **Students' answers may vary, but they should give at least two details for each stage of growth.**

Years Old	Details
10	It is four inches high; ants climb its sides; a pack rat drinks water from the paloverde tree that shades it.
25	It is two feet tall; a jackrabbit gnaws on it.
50	It is ten feet tall; white-and-yellow flowers appear at the top; birds, bees, and bats come for nectar; woodpeckers make holes for nests.
60	The cactus is 18 feet tall; it grows an arm; birds live in it.
150	The cactus stops growing; it is 50 feet tall and weighs eight tons; there are many birds, pack rats, insects, and bats living in holes in the cactus.
200	The cactus falls over; creatures who lived up high leave; new insects move in; snakes and lizards find food in it.

At Home: Have students draw a picture of what the saguaro cactus looks like after 150 years.

Book 3.2/Unit 1
Cactus Hotel 6

Use a Chart

Read the story below. It contains many facts that could be shown in a chart.

Mammals of the Southwest

Many different animals live in the Southwestern states. Some of the mammals are quite different from those that live in other areas. The ringtail has a face like a fox. It is a member of the raccoon family but doesn't have a face mask. It lives among rocks and boulders and is gray with a whitish belly. It is about 2.5 feet long.

If you saw a brown cat with a white belly and black bars on its tail, it was probably a bobcat. Bobcats are about four feet long and live in thickets or among rocks and logs.

Prairie dogs live in a "town" of burrows. They're reddish brown and about fifteen inches long. Some have black tails.

If you hear a terrifying scream near a cave in the mountains, it's probably a mountain lion. This seven-foot-long mammal is a yellowish brown and is also called a cougar.

Now study the chart below. Use the facts from the story to complete the charts.

Mammals of the Southwest

Animals	Length	Where They Live	Color of Animal	Special Feature
Ringtail	2.5 ft.	among rocks and boulders	gray with white belly	face like a fox
Bobcat	4 ft.	thickets, rocks, logs	brown with white belly	black bars on tail
Prairie dog	15 in.	"towns" of burrows	reddish brown	some with black tails
Mountain lion	7 ft.	in caves in mountains	yellowish brown	terrifying scream

---

At Home: Ask students to look up two other desert animals and include them in the chart.

Cause and Effect

Use information from "Cactus Hotel" to complete the cause-and-effect chart below.

Cause

Effects

Fruit falls from a cactus.

1. Then a rat
   <u>eats the fruit</u>   .

2. A seed falls off of the rat's whiskers and lands
   <u>under a tree</u>   .

It rains in the desert.

3. A young cactus
   <u>grows out of the</u>
   <u>ground</u>   .

Flowers appear at the top of the cactus.

4. Birds, bees, and bats see the flowers and
   <u>come to drink nectar</u>
   <u>from them</u>   .

The cactus falls down.

5. The arms of the cactus
   <u>crumble, or fall apart</u>   .

6. The creatures that lived high in the cactus
   <u>must find new homes</u>   .

Sequence of Events

Events in a story happen in a certain **sequence**, or order.

Read the events. For each event, write what you think might happen next. **Answers may vary.**

1. Brian felt very sleepy.

   Brian went to bed. _____

2. The end of Natasha's pencil broke.

   Natasha sharpened her pencil again. _____

3. The class finished eating lunch.

   Everybody went outside for recess. _____

4. Leslie threw the ball.

   Selena caught the ball. _____

5. Frederico opened his present.

   It was a toy plane. _____

6. Amy tried out for the team.

   Amy made the team. _____

7. There was a snowstorm.

   We made a snowman. _____

8. I went to the mall with my dad.

   We had lunch in a restaurant. _____

8 Book 3.2/Unit 1
Cactus Hotel

At Home: Have students choose their favorite
sequence and illustrate it.

131

Suffixes

Suffixes are word parts that can be added to the end of a word. Adding a suffix creates a new word with its own meaning. Sometimes the spelling of the base word changes when a suffix is added. Some common suffixes are listed below.

Some Common Suffixes

Suffix	Meaning	Example
-able	able to be	likable
-ly	in a certain manner	secretly
-y	full of	sandy

Use the chart above for examples of suffixes and their meanings. Write the correct meaning for each word below and use each word in a sentence. **Answers will vary.**

1. comfortable able to feel comfort

   The hat was comfortable.

2. juicy full of juice

   The pear was juicy.

3. slowly in a slow manner

   The car moved slowly.

4. sharply in a sharp manner

   The knife cut the apple sharply.

5. deeply in a deep manner

   The girl dove deeply into the pool.

6. shady full of shade

   It was shady under the tree.

At Home: Challenge students to write two sentences that include all of the words above.

132

Book 3.2/Unit 1
Cactus Hotel

12

Form Generalizations

Below are some generalizations. Read each carefully. Then write down two examples that would lead to the generalization stated. **Answers may vary.**

1. Many animals are furry.

   Dogs are furry.

   Cats are furry.

2. Some students bring lunch from home.

   I bring lunch from home.

   Peter brings lunch from home.

3. Many plants are green.

   Grass is green.

   Ivy is green.

4. Grown men are usually taller than grown women.

   My father is taller than my mother.

   My grandfather is taller than my grandmother.

At Home: Have students write two examples for the generalization, "Many games are played with a ball."

Vocabulary

Tell whether each of the following statements is **true** or **false**.
If it is false, explain why.

1. Babies are older than *adults*.

   <u>False: An adult is someone who is fully grown.</u>

   _____

2. If you *swallow* something, it goes down your throat.

   <u>True.</u>

   _____

3. To *feast* on something means to eat it.

   <u>True</u>

   _____

4. *Mammals* breathe air.

   <u>True.</u>

   _____

5. When there is a storm, the sea is *calm*.

   <u>False: When there is a storm, the waves move a lot. The sea is not</u>

   <u>calm.</u>

6. Two is a *vast* number of people.

   <u>False; "Vast" means "very large."</u>

   _____

At Home: For each false statement above, have students make up a true statement using the vocabulary word.

134

Book 3.2/Unit 1
Big Blue Whale 6

A Whale of a Mural

"Class, today we are going to learn about a new kind of *mammal*," said Miss Linder. "Remember, mammals are animals who give birth to live babies. They don't lay eggs."

"Whales are mammals," said June. "Let's make a *vast* mural to show how big they are!"

The class painted an *adult* whale with a baby whale. Both of the whales were shown in *calm* water. The adult whale had her giant mouth open to *swallow* tiny bits of food.

"You did a great job, class!" said Miss Linder. "Your whale has much food to *feast* on!"

"I worked so hard, I'm as hungry as a whale!" said June.

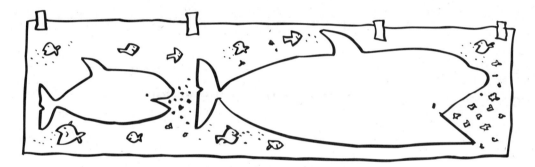

1. What is a fully grown person or animal?

   an adult

2. If water is not rough, what is it?

   calm

3. What is another word for eating a big meal?

   feast

4. How do whales get food from their mouths to their stomachs?

   They swallow.

5. Why might it have been a lot of work for the class to paint the mural?

   Whales are big, and the class wanted to make the mural big, too.

At Home: Have students look up the italicized words from the story in the dictionary. Ask them to copy the definition of each word.

Story Comprehension

Answer the questions below.

1. Why are there so few blue whales in the world?

   There are so few blue whales in the world because people hunted

   and killed so many of them.

2. How large are blue whales?

   Blue whales are the largest creatures that have ever lived on

   Earth. They can grow up to 100 feet long.

3. How do blue whales breathe?

   Blue whales come to the surface of the water to breathe air. They

   breathe air through their blowholes.

4. How long can a blue whale stay under the water?

   A blue whale can stay under the water for at least thirty minutes.

5. How large is the food that blue whales eat?

   The food that blue whales eat is tiny. Whales eat krill, animals that

   are the size of your little finger.

6. Why do blue whales grow fatter in the summer?

   Blue whales grow fatter in the summer because they eat a lot.

   In the winter, whales eat very little.

At Home: Have students write three more sentences
describing how large a blue whale is.

Use a Graph

The bar graph below shows different types of whales in the world.
Use the graph to help you answer the questions that follow.

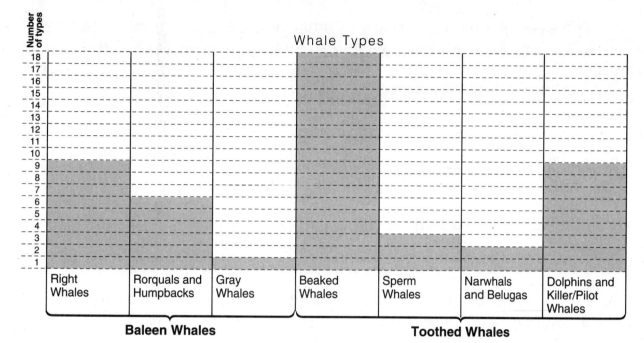

1. Which group of whales contains the largest number of types?

   <u>Beaked</u>

2. How many types of gray whale are there?

   <u>one</u>

3. Is a beaked whale a baleen whale or a toothed whale?

   <u>toothed whale</u>

4. What are the types of baleen whales?

   <u>right whales, rorquals and humpbacks, gray whales</u>

5. How many different types of sperm whales are there?

   <u>three</u>

Form Generalizations

Read the groups of facts below. Make a generalization based on
each group. **Answers may vary.**

1. The eyes of a blue whale are as small as teacups. A grown whale can
    weigh 150 tons. A grown whale can be heavier than 115 giraffes.

    A whale is a giant animal.
    _____

2. A krill is the size of your little finger. It takes millions of krill to feed a
    whale. A krill is only one-half inch to six inches long.

    A krill is a very small animal.
    _____

3. A whale has lungs and breathes air. A whale gives birth to live babies.
    A whale is warm-blooded.

    A whale is a mammal.
    _____

4. Because there isn't much light in deep water, it's hard to see. Whales
    have to use their sense of hearing and their sense of touch to find their
    way in deep water.

    It is dark in deep water.
    _____

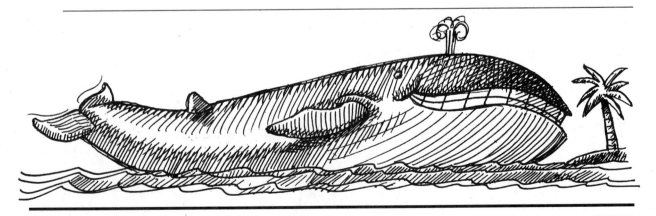

At Home: Have students write one more generalization
about blue whales.

Book 3.2/Unit 1
Big Blue Whale   4

Author's Purpose, Point of View

Read each passage. Is the author trying to **entertain** us, **inform** us of facts, or **persuade** us to do something? Write the author's purpose. Then explain your answer.

Dear Principal,
Our school needs a new gym. The one we have now is too small. During gym class, it gets very crowded in there.
Thank you very much.

Yours,
Genelle Williams

1. I think the author wants to _____persuade._____

2. Reason: _____She is trying to get the school principal to_____

build a new gym._____

Once upon a time, there lived a princess. Well, not exactly a princess. Once upon a time, there lived a little girl who really wanted to be a princess. Every day, the little girl said, "Oh, I would give anything to be a princess."

3. I think the author wants to _____entertain._____

4. Reason: _____The author is telling the beginning of a fairy tale._____

My school has three hundred children and twenty teachers. It is for children in grades five through eight.

5. I think the author wants to _____inform._____

6. Reason: _____The author is telling us facts about his or her school._____

_____

Figurative Language

Colorful words and phrases are called **figurative language**.

One type of figurative language is the **simile**. A simile is a comparison that uses the word **like** or **as**. Here is an example of a simile. The bush was as tall as an elephant.

Another type of figurative language is a **metaphor**. A metaphor is a comparison that does not use the word **like** or **as**. Here's an example of a metaphor. The line snaked through the street.

Read each sentence. Underline the figurative language. On the line beneath, write the meaning of the sentence.

1. We felt the cold breath of winter on our cheeks.

   We felt the cold winter wind._____

2. He heard the leaves on the trees whispering.

   He heard the leaves. They made a quiet, rustling sound._____

   _____

3. The ear of a blue whale is as small as the end of a pencil.

   The ear of a blue whale is very small._____

   _____

4. The blow of a whale is as high as a house.

   The blow of a whale is very tall. It is the height of a house.___

   _____

5. When a blue whale eats, its throat opens out like a huge balloon.

   When a whale eats, its throat opens out in a big puff._____

   _____

At Home: Have students tell whether the figurative language that they underlined in each example above is a simile or a metaphor.

Book 3.2/Unit 1
Big Blue Whale
10

Cause and Effect

Write four possible effects for each cause below. **Answers may vary.**

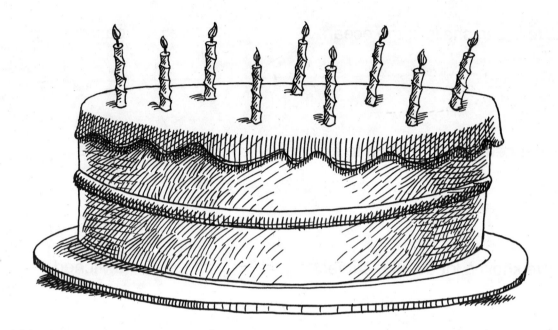

Cause: It is a sunny day.

Effects:

1. I wear shorts. _____

   _____

2. I walk to school. _____

   _____

3. We eat lunch outside. _____

   _____

4. We play games outside. _____

   _____

Cause: It is my birthday.

Effects:

5. People sing "Happy Birthday" to me. _____

6. We eat birthday cake. _____

   _____

7. I blow out the candles. _____

   _____

8. People give me presents. _____

   _____

8 | Book 3.2/Unit 1
J.J.'s Big Day

At Home: Have students write two effects for the
cause "I joined the baseball team."

140

Vocabulary

Draw a line from each clue to the word it describes.

1. We live in shells in the ocean.   gain

2. changed from one thing to another   clams

3. We know a lot about a subject.   switched

4. This happens when we increase
   something.   compared

5. How were things the same?   experts
   How were they different?

6. made into fine, tiny bits ——————————— powdered

141 At Home: Challenge students to use the vocabulary
words in sentences.

Book 3.2/Unit 1
J.J.'s Big Day   6

McGraw-Hill School Division

A Clammy Tale

Once there were two clams. Both *clams* thought they were *experts* at keeping their shells shiny. Every day they *compared* their shells to see whose shined more in the sun.

One day the clams woke up to find that their shells were not shiny at all. They were covered with *powdered* white stuff. Neither had ever seen the white dust before. It was falling from the sky.

The snow was very heavy on the clams' shells. They didn't want to *gain* a lot of weight. "If I *switched* places with those seagulls," one clam shouted, "I wouldn't have this heavy white powder all over me."

"Yes," said the other clam, "but they don't carry around their own house either. We don't have it that bad!"

1. At the beginning of the story, how did the clams pass their time?

   They compared their shells.

2. What did the clams think they were *experts* at doing?

   keeping their shells shiny

3. What was falling from the clouds?

   snow

4. What is a word that describes the white stuff on the clams' shells?

   powdered

5. What birds did the clams talk about?

   seagulls

5 Book 3.2/Unit 1
   J.J.'s Big Day

At Home: Ask students to think of other animals that carry around their own home.

141A

Story Comprehension

Answer these questions about "J.J.'s Big Day."

1. What kind of whale is J.J.?

   J.J. is a gray whale.

2. How old was J.J. when she washed up on the beach?

   J.J. was one week old when she washed up on the beach.

3. What did J.J. drink instead of a mother whale's milk?

   J.J. drank "J.J. shakes" made out of cream, clams, and milk.

4. What were the two problems with returning J.J. to the ocean?

   J.J. had never had to find her own food before. Also, she had not

   been with other whales for a long time.

5. How did the scientists move J.J. back to the ocean?

   The scientists were very careful about moving J.J. back to the

   ocean. She traveled to the beach in a special truck. Once they got

   to the ocean, a boat carried J.J. to a safe spot and put her in the

   ocean.

At Home: Have students write a paragraph describing
J.J.'s first day back in the ocean.

Book 3.2/Unit 1
J.J.'s Big Day

5

McGraw-Hill School Division

Use a Graph

These two graphs show how fishing for whales has changed over the years. The first graph shows that the number of whale hunters and their ships has changed over time. The second graph shows the numbers of whales hunted at three different times.

In the 1980s, almost all hunting for whales was stopped. Now the number of whales in the oceans is increasing again.

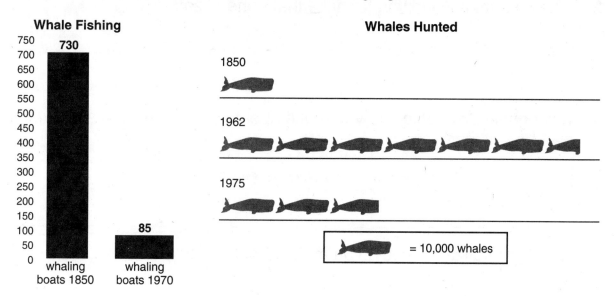

Use the graphs above to answer these questions. **True or False:**

1. The number of whaling boats increased from 1850 to 1970. ___False___

2. The number of whales captured in the 1970s decreased greatly from

   the number captured in the 1960s. ___True___

3. One symbol of a whale stands for 10,000 whales. ___True___

4. If the symbol of the whale is cut in half, it means only half the whale

   was caught. ___False___

4 Book 3.2/Unit 1
J.J.'s Big Day

At Home: Have students read the chart and write a
sentence describing how whale hunting changed
from 1850 to 1975.

143

Form Generalizations

Use the information in "J.J.'s Big Day" to answer the questions below.

1. What generalization could you make about how fast whales grow?

   Whales grow very fast._____

   _____

2. What information led you to make that generalization?

   J.J. gained about two pounds every hour._____

   _____

3. What generalization could you make about where gray whales travel in March?

   In March, gray whales travel north in the Pacific Ocean._____

   _____

4. What generalization could you make about the size of most gray whales?

   Most gray whales are very large._____

   _____

5. What information led you to make that generalization?

   J.J. was very large. She weighed 19,200 pounds and was 31 feet

   long._____

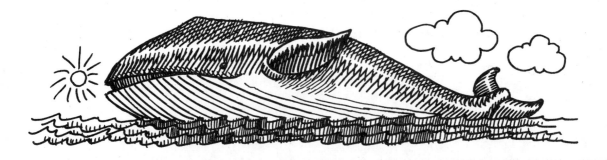

At Home: Have students write a generalization about
what gray whales eat, and explain the information that
144 led them to make that generalization.

Book 3.2/Unit 1
J.J.'s Big Day   5

Figurative Language

Similes use the words **like** or **as** to compare one subject to another.
Metaphors also make comparisons, but without using the words **like** or **as**.

Write **Simile**, **Metaphor**, or **Neither** to describe each sentence.

1. I am as hungry as a horse. _____ Simile

2. His eyes are shining diamonds. _____ Metaphor

3. That dish smells good. _____ Neither

4. I looked out at the ocean of people. _____ Metaphor

5. My skin is as smooth as silk. _____ Simile

6. Johnny laughed on his way home. _____ Neither

7. Annie is as happy as a clam. _____ Simile

8. Paul cried a flood of tears. _____ Metaphor

9. All the animals were hungry. _____ Neither

10. The bear was green with envy. _____ Metaphor

11. My cat is as big as a house. _____ Simile

12. Fishing is more fun than digging. _____ Neither

12 Book 3.2/Unit 1
J. J.'s Big Day

At Home: Give students three subjects, such as a
man dancing, a newly hatched chick, and a girl
running a race. Ask students to write similes or
metaphors that describe each subject.

145

Suffixes

Adding a **suffix** to a word can change its meaning.
The attic is full of <u>dust</u>.

dust + **y** = **dusty**

The attic is **dusty**.

Write the underlined word. Then add the suffix to the underlined word to make a new word.

Rewrite the sentence with the new word.

1. These socks <u>smell</u>.

_____**smell**_____ + y = _____**smelly**_____

These socks are smelly. _____

2. I can <u>wear</u> this shirt.

_____**wear**_____ + able = _____**wearable**_____

This shirt is wearable. _____

3. The boy plays <u>quiet</u> music.

_____**quiet**_____ + ly = _____**quietly**_____

The boy plays music quietly. _____

4. I can <u>read</u> this book.

_____**read**_____ + able = _____**readable**_____

This book is readable. _____

5. The honey <u>sticks</u> to me.

_____**stick**_____ + y =_____**sticky**_____

The honey is sticky. _____

Unit 1 Vocabulary Review

A. Answer each question.

1. **feast**   When would people have a feast? <u>Sample answer: on a</u>
<u>holiday or a birthday</u>

2. **reply**   If you wrote a reply to an invitation, what did you do? <u>Sample</u>
<u>answer: I answered it.</u>

3. **experts**   How do people become experts? <u>Sample answer: They</u>
<u>learn about something.</u>

4. **treat**   If someone wanted to give you a treat, what would you ask for?
<u>Answers will vary.</u>

B. Answer each question with a word from the box.

clams	adult	dozens	comforting	gain	meal

1. Which word means the same as grown-up? _____**adult**_____

2. Which word means the opposite of lose? _____**gain**_____

3. Which word could you use instead of breakfast, lunch, or dinner?

   _____**meal**_____

4. Which word lets you know that there are many of something?

   _____**dozens**_____

5. Which word means making someone feel better? ____**comforting**

6. Which word names things that live in the water? _____**clams**

10 Book 3.2/Unit 1
Unit 1 Vocabulary Review   **At Home:** Have students write a paragraph that uses
the vocabulary words in Part A.   **147**

Unit 1 Vocabulary Review

A. Supply the correct vocabulary word from the box.

relatives	encouraging	swallow

1. Sam's teacher is always _____encouraging_____ him to read more.

2. Mimi's cousins were the only _____relatives_____ at the party.

3. Chew your food well before you _____swallow_____ it.

B. Use words from the list to complete the sentences, then finish the crossword puzzle.

members	discovered	vast	compared	ribs

DOWN

1. _____members_____ belong to a club.

3. Leah _____compared_____ the two books, then chose one.

ACROSS

2. If you found something new, you _____discovered_____ it.

4. The cloth of an umbrella is held in place by its _____ribs_____.

5. Something that is very, very large is _____vast_____.

Crossword:
- 1 Down: M E M B E R S
- 2 Across: D I S C O V E R E D
- 3 Down: C O M P A R E D
- 4 Across: R I B S
- 5 Across: V A S T

Judgments and Decisions

You make a **judgment** or **decision** based on reasons. There may be reasons both for and against something.

Read the story. List reasons for and against. Then answer the questions. **Answers may vary.**

> Dan and his dog spent many afternoons playing ball. Scout could chase and catch a ball almost as fast as Dan could throw one. One day while they were playing in the front yard, Scout barked at a little girl who was riding her bike. The girl was scared and began to cry. Dan's father said that from now on, Dan had to play with Scout inside the fence in the back yard. Dan was unhappy, because there was more room for Scout to chase the ball in the front of the house.

1. Reasons for keeping Scout in the backyard: **The dog barked at a girl and made her cry. He might bite someone next time.**

2. Reasons for letting Scout play in the front yard: **It is more fun to play in the front yard; the dog has more room to run.**

3. What do you think of the decision Dan's father made? **Answers will vary.**

> If Dan trains his dog not to bark at children and to stop running when he says the word "Sit," should Dan's father decide to let Dan and Scout play in the front yard?

4. Reasons for: **Scout will be well trained, and Dan can always make him stop running.**

5. Reasons against: **Scout may make a mistake and bark at a child again.**

5 | Book 3.2/Unit 2
Lon Po Po

At Home: Have students list reasons for and against a personal decision they are trying to make.

149

Vocabulary

Write the correct word from the box to complete each sentence.

claws	delighted	disguised	furious	paced	route

1. I went to the party ___disguised___ as a pirate.

2. The lion was ___furious___ when he saw that he was trapped.

3. I was ___delighted___ when he gave me a new bike.

4. The worried man ___paced___ up and down the room.

5. Shall we bike along the main road or take the shorter ___route___?

6. My cat has sharp ___claws___.

At Home: Have students draw pictures of their own faces illustrating the meanings of the words *delighted* and *furious*.

Book 3.2/Unit 2
Lon Po Po 6

The Trackers

Chad and his father took the same *route* through the woods every day. Chad's father was teaching him about the woods. One day, they came to a tree with strange marks on it.

"Are these marks made by a wolf's *claws*?" Chad asked.

Chad was correct. His father was *delighted* that he was learning about the woods. They walked on. But Chad stopped.

"The leaves are broken," he said. "Something big *paced* through here."

Suddenly, they heard a loud and *furious* sound. Chad and his father covered themselves with branches. Then they moved safely and quickly through the woods *disguised* as trees.

1. What is another word for a path or way to go through the woods?

   a route

2. What are a wolf's sharp nails called?

   claws

3. How did Chad's father feel about him learning about the woods?

   delighted

4. What had an animal done over the broken leaves?

   paced

5. Why were Chad and his father *disguised*?

   To hide from the animal that made the loud noise.

5   Book 3.2/Unit 2
Lon Po Po

At Home: Have students use each of the italicized words from the story in a sentence.

150A

Story Comprehension

Think about "Lon Po Po." Then complete each sentence in the story map below. **Answers may vary.**

When and Where

The story takes place (1.) _long ago_____ ,

somewhere in the country of (2.) _China_____ .

Characters

The five characters are (3.) _Mother, Shang, Tao, Paotze, and the wolf_

_____ .

Story Problem

The wolf wants to (4.) _eat the three children_____ .

To keep safe, the children must (5.) _get the wolf out of their house_ .

_____ .

Story Events

The wolf tricks the children by (6.) _pretending to be their grandmother_ .

The children trick the wolf by (7.) _telling him that nuts from the_

ginkgo tree are magic

How the Problem Is Solved

The wolf (8.) _dies from falling from the tall tree_

_____ .

McGraw-Hill School Division

Read a Newspaper

Read the newspaper story below. Try to decide which statements are opinions.

Alien Craft Lands at Old Faithful?

Donna Eggerton — Aug. 8, 1999: Wolves may not be the only returning visitors to Yellowstone National Park. Campers in the park reported strange sounds and lights last night.

"The roar was like a thousand water-falls," Pearl Johnson explained. "We were camping by the lake. The lights seemed bigger than any spotlights I ever saw."

Last year, hikers in the area reported similar lights and noises. Many rangers felt that city people aren't used to the sights and sounds of the woods at night. "A car's headlights across the lake can look odd," one reported. "And animals in the dark make what may seem like a lot of strange noises."

A nearby Air Force base spokesman said no unidentified flying objects were in the area.

Write each sentence that contains an opinion on the lines. Consider the headline, byline, and quotations. **Answers may vary.**

1. Alien Craft Lands at Old Faithful?

2. "The roar was like a thousand waterfalls, Pearl Johnson explained.

3. "The lights seemed bigger than any spotlights I ever saw."

4. Many rangers felt that city people aren't used to the sights and sounds of the woods at night.

5. "A car's headlights across the lake can look odd," one reported.

6. "And animals in the dark make what may seem like a lot of strange noises."

6 Book 3.2/Unit 2
Lon Po Po

At Home: Have students search a newspaper for a story with opinions and cut it out.

152

Judgments and Decisions

Readers often make judgments about a character's actions. When you make a **judgment,** you decide what you think based on reasons you find in the story.

Read the actions of the characters below and make a judgment about the characters' actions. Then list your reasons. **Answers will vary.**

In "Lon Po Po," the wolf thought he would be able to trick the children by disguising himself as their grandmother.

1. Do you think the wolf was clever? <u>yes or no</u>

List two reasons.

2. <u>Yes: his disguise worked and he got himself into the house.</u>

   <u>No: his disguise didn't work for long.</u>

3. <u>Yes: he came up with answers to Shang's question about</u>

   <u>being late and having a low voice and claws. No: he couldn't</u>

   <u>explain why he wanted to blow out the candle.</u>

Shang decides on a way to trick the wolf. She gets her sisters to help.

4. Do you think Shang made a good decision? <u>Yes.</u>

List two reasons.

5. <u>Shang is clever and has good ideas.</u>

6. <u>She pretends that the children are weak and gets the wolf to help.</u>

At Home: Have students tell how the sisters in "Lon Po Po" first made a bad decision, and then tell how they made a good decision.

153

Book 3.2/Unit 2
Lon Po Po   6

Summarize

When you **summarize** a story, you tell only the most important things that happen. You can also summarize the information in a paragraph.

Summarize each paragraph below in one sentence.

Alice threw away her peach in the trash, but Sam had another idea. He planted the peach pit in the ground. He knew that the seed of the plant was inside the pit. With any luck, the old peach would grow into a tree and produce hundreds of peaches in just a few years.

Summary _Sam tried to grow a peach tree from a peach pit._

Some people like to train dogs; other people like to train plants! It is fun to make shapes out of growing things. People can train plants into the shape of a ball, a tree, or even an animal like a deer. All it takes to train a plant is time and patience.

Summary _People can train plants into shapes like trees or animals._

2 | Book 3.2/Unit 2
Lon Po Po

At Home: Ask students to summarize what they did last summer.

154

Context Clues

There are two kinds of **context clues. General clues** are nearby words. Actual definitions or descriptions of the word in question are called **specific clues.**

Circle the words and phrases that help you tell what the word means. Then write the meaning of the underlined word on the line.

1. The wolf had sharp claws. They felt different from the nails on a human hand.

   sharp nails on the foot of an animal_____

2. I couldn't believe I was really in the desert. It is such a hot, dry, and sandy place.

   hot, dry, sandy place_____

3. I didn't mean to drop the plate. It was an accident.

   something that does not happen on purpose_____

4. I always get names wrong. For instance, I thought that his name was John, but I was mistaken. His name is James.

   wrong_____

5. She always tells the truth. She never tells lies.

   not lies_____

6. He took hold of the shovel tightly with both hands. He had to grasp it or it would drop.

   take hold of something_____

Fact and Nonfact

You can use your own knowledge to decide whether a statement is a **fact** or a **nonfact**. You can try to prove the information is a fact by looking in sources such as an atlas, an encyclopedia, a calendar, or a newspaper article.

Read each statement. Write **fact** if the statement is true. Write **nonfact** if the statement is false. Then tell how you would prove whether the statement is a fact, or a nonfact, or if you can answer from your own experience. **Answers may vary.**

1. It is cold in Los Angeles and all of southern California. ___nonfact___

2. How can you prove it? __experience; an atlas, weather report__

3. No other animal in the world is as colorful as a frog. ___nonfact___

4. How can you prove it? __experience; a book about animals and birds.__

5. Before people had cars, many people used horses to travel from place

    to place. _____fact_____

6. How can you prove it? __history books, an encyclopedia__

7. Many people celebrate Christmas on December 25. _____fact_____

8. How can you prove it? __experience; a calendar__

9. Whales are the biggest animals that swim in the ocean. ___fact___

10. How can you prove it? __an encyclopedia, a book about animals__

10 Book 3.2/Unit 2
Animal Fact/Animal Fable

At Home: Ask students to give you an example of a
fact, and then tell how it could be proved.

156

Vocabulary

Write the correct word from the box to complete each sentence.

rapidly	temperature	label	attack	expects	bother

1. The fighting fish started to _____attack_____ one another.

2. She gets a lot done because she works _____rapidly_____.

3. Please do not _____bother_____ me while I am reading

   or cooking.

4. She knows John is a good cook, so she _____expects_____

   dinner to be delicious.

5. There was a _____label_____ on each sale item.

6. The _____temperature_____ must be high because I feel

   very hot!

At Home: Ask students to use one or two of the vocabulary words in a sentence that describes their local weather.

157

Book 3.2/Unit 2
Animal Fact/Animal Fable

6

The Artist

Rita always drew pictures of things she saw. She also wrote a *label* for each picture. One day her brother Joe said, "Who *expects* to learn from so many pictures? Don't *bother* with all that drawing."

Rita told Joe that she learned a lot from what she drew. "Once I saw a spider *attack* a fly stuck in its web," she said. "The spider moved *rapidly* to trap the fly."

Rita also told Joe about a day when the *temperature* suddenly dropped. Everyone was slipping and sliding on the icy ground.

"My pictures help me remember," she said.

"Then draw a picture of me!" said Joe. "Then you can remember me forever."

"Yuck!" replied Rita. "How could I ever forget you!"

1. How did Rita name each picture?

   <u>**She wrote a label.**</u>

2. What did Joe tell Rita not to *bother* doing?

   <u>**draw so many pictures**</u>

3. How did the spider move to catch the fly?

   <u>**rapidly**</u>

4. What suddenly dropped one day?

   <u>**the temperature**</u>

5. What does Joe ask Rita to do at the end of the story?

   <u>**draw a picture of him**</u>

 5 Book 3.2/Unit 2
Animal Fact /Animal Fable

At Home: Have students draw and label at least three interesting things they have seen recently.

157A

Story Comprehension

Think about the facts and fables you have learned about animals in "Animal Fact/Animal Fable." Then list one fact and one fable for each animal in the chart below. **Answers will vary.**

Fact	Fable
turtle	
1. A turtle's shell is really part of its body.	2. A turtle can walk out of its shell.
cricket	
3. A cricket chirps faster on hot days and slower on cold days.	4. A cricket always tells the exact temperature by its chirps.
porcupine	
5. A porcupine backs up and sticks its quills into an enemy.	6. A porcupine shoots its quills.
dog	
7. A dog can signal how it feels by its tail.	8. A dog can use words to talk.
ostrich	
9. An ostrich may stretch its neck along the ground.	10. An ostrich hides its head in the sand.
goat	
11. A goat prefers to eat plants, but will eat paper and string.	12. A goat will even eat tin cans.

158

At Home: Have students explain how fables might have come about.

Book 3.2/Unit 2
Animal Fact/Animal Fable
12

Read a Newspaper

Judge if the statements below come from a real newspaper. To do this, decide if the statements use facts about animals. If so, write **Fact** beside them. If a statement is only trying to entertain, write **Not Fact**.

1. Bats can almost see in the dark. They have radar that   Fact helps them sense objects even without seeing them.

2. The ostriches were so upset about the terrible weather   Not Fact we've been having, they hid their heads in the sand.

3. The goats were so bored with their meals, they ate   Not Fact tin cans!

4. The arctic tern can fly longer than any other bird.   Fact It flies over 11,000 miles without stopping.

5. The roadrunner bird rarely flies. When surprised,   Fact it runs across the sand at high speed.

6. The roadrunner bird always tricks the silly   Not Fact coyote, who tries to use rocket skates to catch it.

7. A porcupine can shoot its quills like arrows and   Not Fact hit a bull's-eye from 50 yards.

8. The quills on a porcupine are attached loosely and   Fact may shake off if it swings its tail in self-defense.

At Home: Have students write one sentence about birds that is a fact and one sentence that is not a fact.

Fact and Nonfact

A **fact** can be proved to be true. A **nonfact** is a statement that cannot be proved. Remember that a fable is a nonfact.

Use the information you learned in "Animal Fact/Animal Fable" to complete the chart below.

Animal Fables	Animal Facts
1. Turtles walk out of their shells.	2. Turtles stay in their shells until they die.
3. Porcupines shoot their quills.	4. Porcupines back into their enemies and the barbs on their quills stick.
5. Ostriches hide their heads in the sand.	6. Ostriches stretch out their necks along the ground to hide.
7. Goats will eat tin cans.	8. Goats chew the labels on cans to get to the glue underneath.

At Home: Ask students to write a fact and a fable about another animal.

Summarize

When you **summarize**, you tell the most important things that happened. A summary is short and includes only the major events.

Read the story below. Then fill in the chart by writing a sentence that tells about each of the major events in the game.

The soccer game between Team Blue and Team Orange was tied 10 to 10. Andy, who was on Team Blue, ran as fast as he could and kicked the ball. He stubbed his toe, but the ball went into the net and he scored. Now the score was 11 to 10 and Team Blue was ahead.

During time-out, Andy checked his toe to make sure it wasn't hurt. When they went back to the game, Team Orange scored 4 points in a row. Now Team Orange was ahead by 3 points.

There were only a few minutes left to play when it started to rain. Then it started to pour and Mr. Wright called off the game. "We'll have to play each other again next week," he said.

Who played:

1. Team Blue and Team Orange played a soccer game.

The score at the beginning of the story:

2. The score was 10 to 10 at the beginning of the story.

What happened right after Andy's kick:

3. Andy scored and Team Blue was ahead by a point.

How the game ended:

4. The game was rained out, and the teams would play again next week.

At Home: Ask students to explain why the fact that Andy stubbed his toe is not included in the summary.

Context Clues

The two types of **context clues** are **general clues**, such as nearby words and **specific clues**, such as actual definitions of the word in question.

Use context clues to figure out the meaning of the words in dark type. Write the meaning of each word in dark type on the line.

1. This kind of wood feels very **smooth**, but the other kind feels rough.

   not rough

2. **September** is my favorite fall month.

   a fall month

3. I remember when that old dog was still a young **puppy**.

   young dog

4. She can't hear you because she is **deaf**.

   not able to hear

5. May I have the **recipe** for these delicious cookies? I want to learn how to make them.

   a list of directions for making something to eat

6. Do you know her home **address**? I want to send her a letter.

   the place where someone lives

7. The city was **ancient**. It must be at least a thousand years old.

   very old

8. Jane tried to **hurl** the ball high in the air, but it fell quickly to the ground .

   throw something hard

At Home: Have students circle the context clues for each word.

Book 3.2/Unit 2
Animal Fact/Animal Fable

8

Main Idea

The **main idea** of a selection is the most important point, or what the information is about. **Supporting details** are "smaller" points that explain the main idea. Details may include examples, facts, or steps in a process.

Read the paragraphs below. After each, write the main idea and two supporting details. **Answers may vary.**

> The earth is made up of many layers. One layer contains oil, gas, and coal. The layer deep inside the earth is made of iron. It is very hot inside the center of the earth.

1. **Main Idea:** The earth has many layers.

2. **Supporting Detail:** One layer contains oil, gas, and coal.

3. **Supporting Detail:** The layer deep inside the earth is made of iron.

> Although not all types of plants will grow in all places, you can grow many kinds of plants at home by planting a seed. First, fill a pot halfway to the top with soil. Place the seed in the soil and cover it with more soil. Then, water the soil. Some seeds, such as carrot seeds, grow very quickly.

4. **Main Idea:** You can grow many plants at home from seeds.

5. **Supporting Detail:** Place the seed in the soil.

6. **Supporting Detail:** Cover the seed with more soil.

6 | Book 3.2/Unit 2
The Many Lives of Benjamin Franklin

At Home: Have students look in an encyclopedia under "Earth" to find two more supporting details for the main idea: "The earth has many layers."

163

Vocabulary

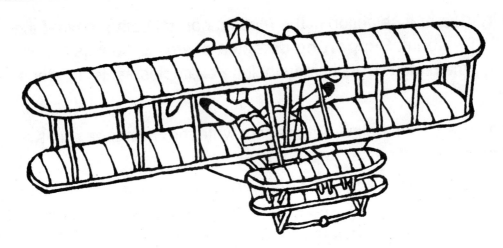

Supply the correct words from the list to complete the sentence.

experiment	curious	scientific	discuss	advice	hero

For thousands of years, people had been _____curious_____ about

birds' ability to fly. It seemed like magic! By the early 1900s, there were

true, _____scientific_____ explanations for the wonder of flight.

Orville and Wilbur Wright believed that they could create machines that

would fly. The brothers did not write about or _____discuss_____ their

ideas with many people. Instead, they followed their dreams, beginning

with a simple _____experiment_____ that led to the world's first flight.

What would you do if you believed in something? Listen to _____advice_____

from other people or go your own way? Sometimes the answers we find

can change the lives of many people. Who knows? Someday you might be

cheered as a _____hero_____ for the discoveries you have made.

At Home: Have students use as many vocabulary words from this page as they can to write another passage.

164

Book 3.2/Unit 2
The Many Lives of Benjamin Franklin

6

A Book About Ben

Sam was *curious* about Ben Franklin. After school one day, he asked the librarian for a book about Franklin.

"Do you want to read about the *advice* he gave in his newspaper?" the librarian asked.

"No," said Sam.

"Do you want to know about Franklin forming the first public library?" the librarian asked.

"No," Sam replied.

"Do you want to know about Franklin's *scientific experiments*?"

"No," said Sam. "I want to find a book that will *discuss* what a great *hero* Franklin was."

The librarian smiled and led Sam to the perfect book.

1. How did Sam feel about Ben Franklin?

   <u>He was curious.</u>

2. What did he first ask the librarian for?

   <u>a book about Benjamin Franklin</u>

3. What did Ben Franklin give in the newspaper?

   <u>advice</u>

4. What kind of *experiments* did Ben Franklin do?

   <u>scientific experiments</u>

5. What type of book did Sam want?

   <u>one that discussed what a great hero Franklin was</u>

Book 3.2/Unit 2
The Many Lives of Benjamin Franklin

At Home: Have students name someone they would like to read about. Then have them write about why they think this person is important.

164A

Story Comprehension

Complete the chart by listing details of some important things that
Ben Franklin did during each time period. **Answers may vary.**

Time Period	Details About Accomplishments
Franklin's early years in Boston.	He held on to a kite string and the kite pulled him across the water while he was swimming. He learned the printing trade. He wrote stories and essays.
Franklin in Philadelphia from age 17 to age 42.	He bought his own print shop. He printed a newspaper and a popular calendar, *Poor Richard's Almanack*. He started police and fire departments, a hospital, and the first free lending-library in America.
Franklin in Philadelphia from age 42 until he left for England.	He proved that lightning was electricity. He invented the lightning rod, the Franklin stove, a musical instrument, and bifocals.
Franklin in England, France, and America until his death at age 84.	He helped write the Declaration of Independence, and he got France to help during the Revolutionary War. He was the first governor of Pennsylvania, and he helped to write the U.S. Constitution.

At Home: Have students write about the period of Franklin's life that is most interesting to them.

Book 3.2/Unit 2
The Many Lives of Benjamin Franklin

4

Follow Directions

Ben Franklin's early experiments in electricity paved the way for others. In 1825, Joseph Henry and William Sturgeon each created electromagnets.

You can make a simple one yourself. The directions below will show you how to do this. But they're all mixed up. There's a clue in every direction that will help you put them in the correct order. Number them correctly.

Note: If you'd like to try this experiment, ask an adult to help you.

___6___ As a last step, hold the nail over the pins or clips. Then touch the second end of the wire to the other battery terminal.

___1___ Gather these things to start: a 3-inch nail, 10 feet of insulated copper wire, a 6-volt battery, a few small paper clips, tacks, pins, or other small metal objects.

___3___ The third thing to do is to put a piece of tape around the wound wire to keep it in place. The wire must be wound around the nail before you can do this step.

___4___ After you've put the tape around the wire on the nail, strip the rubber insulation off the ends of both wires. Do not wind them around the nail.

___2___ The second step is to begin to wind the wire around the nail. Leave about 1 foot of wire loose. Then wind the wire tightly from one end to the other. Leave another 1 foot of wire loose at the other end. Always wind in the same direction.

___5___ The next-to-last step is to connect one end of the stripped wire to one end of the battery terminal.

Results: You'll see the nail become a magnet and lift up the pins. Take one wire off the battery and you'll see the pins drop back down. Electricity has made the nail into a magnet.

Main Idea

When you read nonfiction, try to identify the **main ideas** and **supporting details** to help you understand what you are reading.

Look through "The Many Lives of Benjamin Franklin." List four supporting details for each main idea. **Answers may vary.**

Main Idea: Benjamin Franklin was an inventor who made many discoveries.

Supporting Details

1. He invented bifocals, the lightning rod, and the Franklin stove.

2. He experimented with new ways to grow crops.

3. He made a scientific experiment that proved that lightning is electricity.

4. He discovered that black cloth keeps people warmer than white cloth.

Main Idea: Franklin helped the American colonies win their independence from England and form a new government.

Supporting Details

5. He stayed in England for 18 years working for American independence.

6. He signed the Declaration of Independence.

7. He went to France to ask the French king to help America.

8. He helped write the United States Constitution.

At Home: Have students write the main idea and three supporting details for the story "The Many Lives of Benjamin Franklin."

167

Book 3.2/Unit 2
The Many Lives of Benjamin Franklin

8

Judgments and Decisions

Readers make **judgments** about story characters based on what they do and say.

Read the story and make a judgment about each character. Then list the reasons for your judgment. **Answers may vary.**

The school play was to begin at 7 o'clock and Chang was trying to fix his costume. Then his little sister Ana ran into his room making an awful howling sound, and Chang stuck his finger with a pin.

"Ana! I'm busy. What's wrong?" he said, trying not to sound cross .

"No one will read to me. You read to me," she demanded. Chang said he was busy but that she could stay in his room if she would be quiet. Ana started howling again.

"OK, we'll play a game," Chang said. "If you help get my costume together, then I'll read."

Ana stopped crying and nodded yes.

Chang told her what he needed. Ana flew to the closet. Soon she had all the pieces of the costume piled neatly on Chang's bed.

1. Do you think that Chang was a good older brother? _____ **Yes.**

Reasons why:

2. <u>He tried not to sound cross when Ana came howling into the room.</u>

_____

3. <u>He thought of a game so that he would have time to read to her.</u>

4. What did you think of Ana before Chang said they would play a game?

<u>Ana was irritating.</u>

Reason why:

5. <u>She was howling and running into Chang's room.</u>

5 Book 3.2/Unit 2
The Many Lives of Benjamin Franklin

At Home: Ask students to write about a favorite story character and give some reasons why they like the character.

168

Root Words

Many of the words we use in English today are borrowed from two very old languages—Latin and Greek.

Each word below comes from the Latin word *scribere*, which means "to write." Complete each sentence using *script* or *scribble*. Then write the meaning of the word on the line below.

script   scribble

1. I didn't have much time, so I had to _____scribble_____ him a note.

   Meaning: to write quickly_____

2. Our teacher says that, after we learn how to print letters, she'll teach us

   how to write in _____script_____.

   Meaning: a type of writing_____

Each word below comes from the Latin word *populus*, which means "people." Complete each sentence using *popular* or *public*. Then write the meaning of the word on the line below.

popular   public

3. Anyone can use a _____public_____ beach.

   Meaning: for all the people_____

4. Everyone liked that book—it was very _____popular_____

   Meaning: liked by many people_____

At Home: Have students think of other words that have their roots in *scribere* or *populus*. Then have students tell what the words mean.

169

Book 3.2/Unit 2
The Many Lives of Benjamin Franklin
8

Summarize

A **summary** is a brief statement that tells the main ideas or events of a selection.

Read the following story.

> Toni's birthday was in one week. Toni gave the list of girls she wanted to invite to her party to her mother.
>
> "Where is Sarah's name? Certainly you want to ask your best friend," her mother said as she went to fix dinner.
>
> The truth was, Toni didn't feel like asking Sarah. Lately, Sarah was always walking home from school with May, a girl who had just started going to their school.
>
> The day before the party, Sarah looked for Toni in the playground. "Happy birthday tomorrow," Sarah said.
>
> "I hope we're still friends," Sarah continued. "You know, May would like to be your friend, too. She doesn't know very many people yet."
>
> "She would? I thought you two were ignoring me," Toni said. "Well, why don't you both come over tomorrow?"
>
> Later, Toni asked her mother if she could invite 11 people to her party.
>
> "And maybe when I'm 11 I won't be so silly," she thought to herself.

Write a paragraph to summarize the main events in the story. Be sure to answer the following questions : What is Toni's problem? What does Sarah do? What does Toni do then? **Answers will vary.**

Toni didn't invite her best friend Sarah to her birthday party. She

thought Sarah was ignoring her. When Sarah wished Toni a happy

birthday, she told her she hoped they were still friends. Toni

invited Sarah and May to her party. She asked her mother if they

could have 11 people at the party.

 Book 3.2/Unit 2
Cloudy With a Chance of Meatballs
At Home: Ask students to explain how they chose the information in their summary.
170

Vocabulary

Write words from the box that mean almost the same thing as the underlined word or words.

avoid	brief	frequently	gradual	periods	report

1. I live in a place where it rains <u>often</u>. _____**frequently**_____

2. We heard an <u>announcement</u> on the radio that it would rain all day.

   _____**report**_____

3. Last year, there were several <u>times</u> when we had no rain at all.

   _____**periods**_____

4. I <u>keep away</u> from the roads because I don't want to be splashed by

   cars. _____**avoid**_____

5. My brother did not take his

   umbrella because he saw a

   <u>slow</u> clearing in the sky.

   _____**gradual**_____

6. Sometimes the showers are <u>short</u>,

   but today it rained all day.

   _____**brief**_____

At Home: Have students use each of the words they wrote in a new sentence.

Book 3.2/Unit 2
Cloudy With a Chance of Meatballs 6

McGraw-Hill School Division

The Weather Kids

It had rained every day for a week. Julia and Roy had to play inside. To *avoid* becoming bored, they pretended they were weather reporters.

First, Roy gave a *brief* weather *report*. He said that it would rain *frequently*.

Then Julia looked out the window and said, "There will be *periods* of rain with a *gradual* turning to snow."

Suddenly, Roy and Julia saw a rainbow and blue skies.

Roy gave one final report: "By the end of the day expect clearing skies." Julia laughed and the two headed outside. Finally they would be able to finish planting their spring garden.

1. What did Julia and Roy want to *avoid*?

   becoming bored

2. What was Roy's weather *report* like?

   brief

3. In Roy's *report*, how often was it going to rain?

   frequently

4. How was the change from rain to snow going to be?

   gradual

5. Why did Roy say to expect clearing skies?

   The skies were blue and a rainbow appeared.

Book 3.2/Unit 2
Cloudy With a Chance of Meatballs

At Home: Encourage the students to talk about their favorite kinds of weather. What makes that kind of weather special or fun?

171A

Story Comprehension

In "Cloudy With a Chance of Meatballs," Grandpa tells a bedtime story to the two children. Like most stories, Grandpa's tall tale about Chewandswallow involves a problem and a solution. The point where the main character or characters begin to solve the problem is the **turning point** of the story. Reread the story. Use what you read to fill in the chart. **Answers will vary**.

	Plot Event	**Explain**
Problem	1. What is Chewandswallow's problem? bad food	They cannot control what food falls.
	2. How does it get worse? food chokes town	The food clogs the streets. Terrible food storms occur. A huge pancake covers the school. Maple syrup floods the town. Everyone gets stomachaches. The town is a mess.
Solution	3. What is the turning point? people decide to flee	People can't go outside. The school closes. Houses are damaged. People fear for their lives.
	4. What action do people take to solve the problem? build boats	They sail to a new land on rafts made from stale bread.
	5. Is the problem solved? Yes	The new town welcomes them. The people use the bread to build houses. They buy their food at the supermarket.

At Home: Ask students to tell about something that has changed in their life. Have them explain how things were before and how they are different now.

172

Book 3.2/Unit 2
Cloudy With a Chance of Meatballs
10

Read Signs

Study the signs. Then read the statement about each sign.
Is it **True** or **False**? Write your answer in the space on the right.

1. This sign is saying you can
   park all day on Monday.   _____True_____

2. This sign warns you that
   traffic from two roads will come
   together into one road.   _____True_____

3. This sign is telling you that the
   road will split in two up ahead.   _____True_____

4. This sign is telling you that anyone
   can park here.   _____False_____

5. This sign is telling you where you
   can buy a kite for flying.   _____False_____

6. This sign is saying that you can't
   walk here.   _____False_____

6 Book 3.2/Unit 2
Cloudy With a Chance of Meatballs
At Home: Have students draw a traffic sign and tell
what it means.
173

Summarize

When you **summarize**, you tell the most important things that happened. A summary does not include small details.

Imagine that you are writing a report about "Cloudy With a Chance of Meatballs" for your school book fair. Write two paragraphs that summarize the story for your readers. Include only the most important parts of the story. **Answers will vary.**

Grandpa tells his grandchildren a story about a town named

Chewandswallow. In this town, the people got their food by going

outside and collecting whatever had rained down from the sky. They

were used to getting nice things to eat. Suddenly the weather

changed, and they were being flooded by food like maple syrup. They

could no longer clean up the extra food that came down.

   Finally they decided they had to get away. They built a boat with

bread and sailed away to a new town where they had to learn how to

go to the store and shop for food off the shelves. The day after they

heard the story, the grandchildren went sledding. While they were

outside, they imagined that the snow was mashed potatoes.

At Home: Ask students to tell you about the part of the story that they liked most.

McGraw-Hill School Division

Judgments and Decisions

People use the information that they have to make **judgments** and to **decide** what to do.

Read the following passages. List the reasons for and against each decision and then tell what you would do.

Last night it snowed for the first time this winter. You want to go sleigh riding with your friends. Unfortunately, you have a sore throat. What should you do?

Reasons for going sleigh riding:

1. It would be fun. You want to see your friends. Your sore throat probably won't get much worse.

Reason against going sleigh riding:

2. You should stay home and take care of your sore throat.

3. What would you do? Answers may vary.

Imagine that your family just moved to a new town. Although you miss your friends from your old town, you are eager to make new friends. This coming weekend, you have been invited to two parties. One is with your old friends. The other is with people you have just met in your new town. You are having trouble deciding which party to attend.

Reason for going to the party with your old friends:

4. You miss your old friends, and you want to see them.

Reason for going to the party with people in your new town:

5. You want to make friends in your new town.

6. What would you do? Answers may vary.

6 Book 3.2/Unit 2
Cloudy With a Chance of Meatballs

At Home: Have students write about ways that they could stay friends with people from an old town and also make friends in a new town.

175

Root Words

Many English words come from Greek and Latin.

Each word below comes from the Latin word *cor,* which means "heart." Complete each sentence with the correct word.

discouraged   encouraged   courage

1. My teacher _____ **encouraged** _____ me.

   She said that I was doing a good job.

2. After losing the race, I felt very sad and _____ **discouraged** _____.

3. She is very brave. I would like to have as much __ **courage** __ as she has.

Each word below comes from the Latin word *specere* which means "to look." Complete each sentence with the correct word.

spectacle   respect   expecting

4. Come in. I have been _____ **expecting** _____ you.

5. He is a great person. I _____ **respect** _____ him.

6. Did you see the show? It was quite a _____ **spectacle** _____.

176   **At Home:** Have students write definitions for the six words above.

Book 3.2/Unit 2
Cloudy With a Chance of Meatballs   6

Main Idea

The **main idea** is the most important point that an author wants readers to understand. **Supporting details** are the smaller examples and reasons that explain more about the main idea.

Read the following selection. List the supporting details that give more information about the main idea.

Amy Tan is a Chinese-American writer. Her parents were born in China, but she was born in California. Even when she was very young, people thought that she would become a good writer.

Amy Tan uses her own experiences to write her stories. Some of her stories tell what it is like to grow up in a Chinese family in America. In the book, *The Joy Luck Club*, she tells about a nine-year-old girl.

Amy Tan writes that the girl thinks her mother's Chinese customs are sometimes strange. Still, she listens to her mother's advice.

Main Idea: Amy Tan uses her own experience to write about being a Chinese American.

Supporting Details:

1. Tan's parents were born in China. She was born in California.

2. Tan writes about growing up in a Chinese family in America.

3. The girl in *The Joy Luck Club* thinks her mother's Chinese

   customs are sometimes strange.

4. The girl in *The Joy Luck Club* listens to her mother's advice.

Vocabulary

Answer **yes** or **no** to each question. Then explain your answer by writing a definition for the underlined word. **Answers will vary**.

energy	pollution	future	entire	model	produce

1. Is electricity a kind of <u>energy</u>? Yes. Energy is the capacity for action or doing work.

2. If it took the <u>entire</u> family to push the car, does that mean that even the kids helped? Yes. Entire means all of something.

3. Is there such thing as good <u>pollution</u>? No. Pollution is harmful because it dirties the air, water, and soil.

4. Are flowers something that rose bushes <u>produce</u>? Yes. Produce means to create or bring something into being.

5. Is the past the same thing as the <u>future</u>? No. The past is time that has already gone by. The future is time that has yet to come.

6. Is a real airplane a small copy of a <u>model</u> airplane? No. A model airplane is a small copy of a real airplane.

At Home: Have students use two or three of the vocabulary words in new sentences.

Book 3.2/Unit 2
Pure Power! 6

Teacher for the Future

David Edwards was planning his *future*. He drew a picture of what he would be when he grew up. Below the picture, he wrote, "I will be a *model* science teacher for the *entire* school."

David was concerned with natural resources and the environment. He hoped to teach people new ways to *produce energy*.

David also wanted to teach his students about *pollution*. He had several ideas for community clean-up projects. One project was to clean up all the trash near the stream downtown. Another project was to start a glass and plastic recycling center.

David's father was a farmer. From his father David had learned that it was important to take care of the world in which we live.

I will be a model science teacher for the entire school.

1. What did David want to be in the *future*?

   a model science teacher

2. How many students would David teach?

   the entire school

3. What did David hope to teach people to *produce*?

   energy

4. What else did David want to teach about?

   pollution

5. How did David show he cared about the community?

   He had ideas for community clean-up and recycling projects.

Story Comprehension

Answer the following questions about "Pure Power!"

1. What is the main idea in "Pure Power!"? In the future people may use energy from the sun and the wind, because fossil fuels will run out someday .

2. Why are gas, coal, and oil called fossil fuels? They were formed from the fossils or remains of animals and plants from long ago.

3. Where does solar power come from? the sun

4. Where does a lot of the world's pollution come from? from burning fossil fuels

5. How could sun power and wind power help keep the planet clean? Power from the sun and the wind does not cause pollution.

6. What is a solar farm? It is a group of panels that collect sunlight so it can be turned into power.

7. Why might a family want to put tiles on the roof of their house to catch sunlight ? The tiles can turn the sunlight into enough electricity for the needs of a family.

8. Why have people built windmills? A windmill can catch wind and turn it into electricity.

At Home: Ask students to write what they learned about new forms of energy from reading "Pure Power!"

179

Book 3.2/Unit 2
Pure Power!

8

McGraw-Hill School Division

Read an Ad

Compare the following advertisements. See how they use different ideas to interest you. Write **A** or **B** to answer each question.

A.

The Tree of Life Makes Your Life Easier

Eco Products introduces a New and Improved Plastic Bag Recycler. Dry your used plastic bags easily after they are cleaned. **Only $7.99**

Call: 1-800-555-5555 to order your Tree of Life

ECO PRODUCTS MAKE CENTS!

B.

Are you throwing away your money?

Recycle your cans and bottles!

brought to you as a public service by the Ad Group.

Making America Energy Efficient!

1. Which ad is selling a product?   <u>A</u>

2. Which one is selling an idea?   <u>B</u>

3. Which ad is trying to get you to cooperate in a public service?

   <u>B</u>

4. Which ad encourages you to buy something?   <u>A</u>

5. Which ad is brought to you by the Ad Group?   <u>B</u>

6. Which ad (or ads) suggests it has a way to save you money?

   <u>A and B</u>

6 Book 3.2/Unit 2
Pure Power!

At Home: Have students make up their own ad for an ecological product.

180

Fact and Nonfact

Decide whether each statement is a **fact** or an **opinion**. For facts, explain how to prove them to be true—for example, by using a book or an encyclopedia, by asking an expert, or by seeing something firsthand. **Answers may vary.**

1. People need to find new forms of energy because we will run out of coal and oil in the future. **Fact: science books, encyclopedias,** **experts**

2. In Japan some houses have roofs built with tiles that collect sunlight. **Fact: Check by talking to people who make solar tiles or who** **build houses in Japan.**

3. New kinds of windmills can catch more wind than the old ones. **Fact: science book**

4. Eggs taste better when they are cooked by sun power. **opinion**

5. Fossil fuels are formed from the fossils of plants and animals that lived millions of years ago. **Fact: science book**

6. Someday, cars may run on energy made from the sun. **opinion**

At Home: Have students give an example of a fact and an opinion about energy.   Book 3.2/Unit 2 **Pure Power!** 6

Root Words

Knowing the **etymology**, or history, of a word can help you figure out the meaning.

Read about the **root words** below. Then write the meaning for the word in dark type. If you are having trouble, look the word up in a dictionary.

1. **Perfect** comes from the Latin *per*, "completely," and *facere*, "to make."

   fully formed

2. **Contact** comes from the Latin *con*, "together," and *tangere*, "touch."

   a touching or meeting

3. **Auditorium** comes from the Latin *audire*, "to hear," and *orium*, "a place for."

   a place for hearing; a large room where a group of people can

   gather

4. **Disappear** comes from the Latin *dis*, "to do away with something that has been done," and *apparere*, "come into view."

   to go out of sight

5. **Excite** comes from the Latin *ex*, "out," and *ciere*, "to call."

   to stir up

6. **Introduce** comes from the Latin *intro*, "to the inside," and *ducere*, "to lead."

   to bring into use, knowledge, or notice

6 Book 3.2/Unit 2
Pure Power! **At Home:** Have students try to write one sentence
that includes three of the words above. **182**

Context Clues

To figure out the meaning of an unfamiliar word, try reading the words around it.

Match the word in dark type in each sentence in the left-hand column with its definition in the right-hand column. Write the letter of the definition on the line.

__b__ 1. Yesterday, we had no school because of the **storm**. It snowed all day long.

  a. a large bird with black feathers

__c__ 2. That shirt is too **expensive**. I want one that doesn't cost so much.

  b. a strong wind with snow or rain

__e__ 3. The children were very **noisy**. Their father said, "Quiet down, kids. You're being too loud!"

  c. having a high price

__a__ 4. I saw a huge black **crow** flying outside. It was the biggest bird I had ever seen.

  d. time to come

__f__ 5. We grow flowers in our **garden**, but some people grow vegetables instead.

  e. loud

__d__ 6. In the **future**, there will be more bicycles, just you wait and see!

  f. a piece of ground where flowers or vegetables are grown

At Home: Have students underline the context clues in each sentence.

Book 3.2/Unit 2
Pure Power! 6

Unit 2 Vocabulary Review

A. If the underlined word means almost the same as the vocabulary word, write **S** on the line. If it means the opposite, write **O**.

1. **entire**   Lu Yee read the whole book in a week. __S__

2. **frequently**   Roy often stays with his grandmother. __S__

3. **brief**   Wanda took a long rest. __O__

4. **delighted**   Jenny was glad to see her friend. __S__

5. **rapidly**   Ellen walked home slowly. __O__

6. **curious**   The nosy child peeked in the closet. __S__

B. Read each question. Then choose a word from the box to answer each question. Write your answer on the line.

hero	pollution	route	temperature

1. If people throw garbage in the river, what will they cause?

   pollution

2. If you did a brave thing, what would you be?

   hero

3. If you check how hot it is outside, what would you measure?

   temperature

4. If you followed certain streets to get to school, what would you have?

   route

At Home: Have students write a story about an adventure they had. Encourage them to use at least three vocabulary words in their story.

Unit 2 Vocabulary Review

A. Supply the correct vocabulary word.

future	model	label	furious	discuss

1. The _____**label**_____ on the shirt tells what size it is.

2. We always _____**discuss**_____ the stories we read at school.

3. When Carl's little sister broke his kite, he was _____**furious**_____.

4. Alice likes to build _____**model**_____ boats.

5. Since this is winter, summer is in the _____**future**_____.

B. Answer the questions. Then explain your answer by telling what the word means.

1. Which is scientific, to guess what will happen or to figure it out?

   Figure it out; to be scientific, you need to use facts.

2. If companies produce stuffed animals, do they make or sell them?

   Make; produce means "to make something."

3. Could an animal with claws scratch or bite you? **Scratch; claws**

   are sharp nails on an animal.

4. When something is gradual, is it fast or slow? **Slow; gradual**

   means "small changes."

5. If things are disguised, are they hidden or recognized? **Hidden;**

   disguised means "to change the way things look."

At Home: Have students write questions for the vocabulary words in Part A. They can use the questions in Part B as a guide.

Make Inferences

Sometimes an author tells you plainly what is happening in a story. At other times, readers must **infer**, or figure out, what is happening. Readers look for clues the author gives that **show** what is happening.

Read the following passages. Look for clues in each passage to help answer the questions.

> Grandpa John cleaned and polished his old car until it shone like a new penny. He spent all morning on it, and in the afternoon he planned to work on the motor.

1. How does Grandpa feel about his car? **He likes it and wants to make it work.**

2. Explain how you know. **He polishes it and is going to work on the motor.**

> The white peaks got higher and higher. They could change shape in a second—now they were rolling, snowy mountains. Alex took a taste. He put in more sugar and cream. Then he whipped up some clouds in the big blue bowl.

3. What is Alex doing ? **Alex is making whipped cream or whipping sugar and cream.**

4. Explain how you know. **Alex tastes it and puts more sugar and cream in a bowl. Also, Alex is whipping up white snowy "mountains."**

5. How does the author show that Alex has a good imagination? **by telling that Alex imagines food as mountains, snow, and clouds**

5 Book 3.2/Unit 3
The Bat Boy and His Violin

At Home: Have students explain what it means to make inferences.

186

Vocabulary

Write words from the list to complete the story.

accept	equipment	invisible	mistakes	perform	talented

We have a cooking club at our school. On Friday, Ms. Parker showed us how to bake bread. She is a _____**talented**_____ baker who knows how to make all kinds of breads, cakes, and pies. We were lucky to be able to see her _____**perform**_____.

First she gathered her bowls, pans, and other **equipment**. Then she mixed yeast and warm water. "Don't make any _____**mistakes**_____ here," she said. "If the water is too hot, the yeast won't work."

Ms. Parker mixed the yeast with flour to make dough. "You can't see the yeast now," she said. "But even though it's _____**invisible**_____, it's hard at work making the dough rise." She was right. Soon that dough was twice as big as before. And the bread Ms. Parker baked from it was delicious.

So come join our cooking club! We are always happy to _____**accept**_____ new members. You will learn a lot and have fun, too.

At Home: Have students make up one question about the story that could be answered **Yes** and one question that could be answered **No**.

187

Book 3.2/Unit 3
The Bat Boy and His Violin

6

No Mistake About It

Joy loved baseball, but she did not feel *talented* enough to play. She also felt too shy to *perform* in front of fans.

Sometimes Joy carried *equipment* onto the field for the Aces, her older sister's team. Joy carried the bats, gloves, and balls. But once on the field, she felt *invisible*. It was as though no one saw her.

Joy wished that the Aces would *accept* her as a member of the team. Joy really wanted to be more than a team helper.

One Saturday, Joy's wish came true. Her sister had a cold and couldn't play in the game. Joy took her place. And without making any *mistakes*, she led the Aces to win the game!

1. What are some kinds of *equipment* used in baseball?

   gloves, balls, bats

2. How did Joy feel once she got on the field and no one saw her?

   invisible

3. What did Joy wish the Aces would do?

   accept her as a member of the team

4. What did Joy do without any mistakes?

   She led the Aces to win the game.

5. How do you think Joy *performed* in the game?

   She performed well because she did not make any mistakes.

5 Book 3.2/Unit 3
The Bat Boy and His Violin

At Home: Encourage students to talk about a time they felt shy. Why did they feel that way? What helped them feel less shy?

(187A)

Story Comprehension

Think about "The Bat Boy and His Violin." Then complete the chart below.
Answers may vary.

1. **Setting of story**	summertime, 1948; baseball fields, bus, Reginald's house
2. **Main characters**	Reginald, Reginald's father, members of the Dukes baseball team
3. **Beginning of story**	Reginald's father wants Reginald to help the Dukes by being a bat boy. Reginald makes mistakes; he gives too many bats and he polishes the bats. His father takes over.
4. **Middle of story**	Reginald plays the violin while the Dukes play. The music helps the Dukes make hits and win games.
5. **End of story**	The Dukes travel to play the Monarchs and are not allowed to stay in a hotel. Reginald plays his violin to help them sleep. Reginald plays during the game but the Dukes lose. Reginald's father says he is proud of him, and Reginald gives a violin recital at home. The whole team comes to listen.

Use the Library

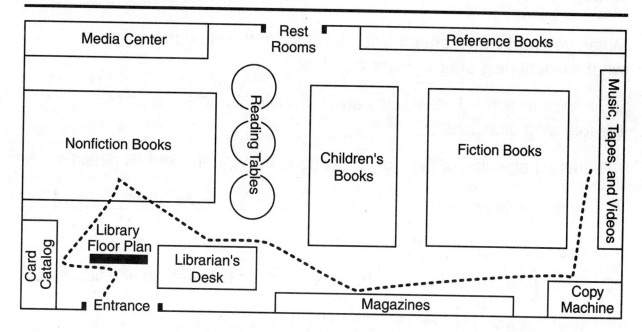

Write down the area of the library visited by the student to complete her task.

1. I look up *piano* and see 786.2 B for the book *Pianos*, by Hal Barber.

   Card Catalog_____

2. I find the 700s on the shelves of books. The book is checked out.

   Nonfiction Books_____

3. I go to the librarian. She suggests a magazine called *Modern Piano*.

   Librarian's Desk_____

4. In this magazine I find a great article about a piano factory.

   Magazines_____

5. I decide to make a copy to take home for my report.

   Copy Machine_____

6. I pick up a tape of great piano music to hear modern pianos.

   Music, Tapes, and Videos

6 Book 3.2/Unit 3
The Bat Boy and His Violin   **At Home:** Ask students to tell where they go first
when they visit the library.   **189**

Make Inferences

When you **make inferences**, you use clues in the story that show what is happening or how characters feel.

Look back through "The Bat Boy and His Violin" to help you answer the following questions.

1. In the beginning of the story, how does Papa feel about Reginald's violin playing? He thinks it keeps Reginald inside too much and hopes Reginald might decide to become a baseball player.

2. Explain what Reginald's father says or does that helped you figure out your answer. He makes noise while Reginald plays; says he should be outside more and that he can practice between innings; he thinks being a bat boy might encourage Reginald to become a baseball player.

3. At the beginning of the story, does Papa think that Reginald is a good bat boy? Explain your answer. No, Reginald has been making too many mistakes. He gives one batter too many bats, and then he polishes the bats.

4. Is Papa surprised when they can't find a hotel that will let the baseball team stay overnight? Explain your answer. No; he just thanks the clerk. It seems as though they have slept in their bus and cooked out before.

5. At the end of the story, why is Reginald afraid that his father won't like his music anymore? The team lost.

At Home: Ask students to explain how Papa's feelings about Reginald's playing the violin change during the story.

190

Book 3.2/Unit 3
The Bat Boy and His Violin

5

Author's Purpose, Point of View

An author's main **purpose** in writing may be to inform, to entertain, or to persuade. Read each passage. Write the author's main purpose. Then evaluate the author's **point of view**.

> You should go to the circus. I went last night. It was so exciting! First, a clown shot out of the dark, jumped on a horse's back, and did tricks. Then he chose a boy from the audience and gave him a scarf. Next the clown tugged at the scarf and a bird flew out of it. The Big Clown Circus will be at City Center for two weeks. I plan to go again!

1. What is the author's main purpose? Explain. <u>The main purpose is to</u>

   <u>persuade readers to go to the circus.</u>

2. What do you think is the author's point of view about the circus? Why?

   <u>The author thinks it is exciting and a lot of fun, and he or she</u>

   <u>wants to go again.</u>

> This is how to make a very tasty fruit salad. Use fruits that you like, such as apples, berries, bananas, or watermelon. Wash all the fruit and cut it up into small pieces. Put the cut-up fruit into a bowl. Make sure you don't get any seeds in the bowl. Then cut an orange in half. Squeeze each half of the orange over the fruit and stir.

3. What is the author's main purpose? Explain. <u>To inform; the author</u>

   <u>tells how to make a fruit salad.</u>

4. Does the author seem to think that it is worth the trouble to make fruit

   salad? What in the passage makes you answer as you did? <u>Yes; the</u>

   <u>author says the fruit salad is very tasty.</u>

4 Book 3.2/Unit 3
The Bat Boy and His Violin

At Home: Ask students to find a story or article that was written for the purpose of entertaining an audience.

191

Multiple-Meaning Words

Multiple-meaning words have more than one meaning. The words and sentences around a word are **context clues**.

Use context clues in each sentence to find the meaning of the underlined word. Circle the letter of the best meaning. Then write a sentence for each multiple-meaning word using a **different** meaning of the word.

1. They cut through the field instead of walking around it.

   a. to divide with something sharp   **b.** to cross or pass

   Possible answer: I cut the cake into eight pieces._____

2. It's hot in here—let's turn on the fan.

   a. something that is used to move   **b.** a person who is very
   the air   enthusiastic about something

   Possible answer: My sister is a huge baseball fan._____

3. I'm learning how to fence. It's a hard sport.

   a. something that is used to   **b.** the sport of fighting with
   mark off an area   a sword

   Possible answer: I painted our fence yellow._____

4. The fly buzzed around my head.

   a. an insect with two wings   **b.** to move through the air

   Possible answer: I watched the birds fly across the sky._____

5. The audience cheered and gave the singer a big hand.

   a. the end part of the arm   **b.** clapping

   Possible answer: I hurt my hand while playing baseball._____

At Home: Have students underline the context clue that helped them to define the underlined word in each sentence.

192

Book 3.2/Unit 3
The Bat Boy and His Violin

10

Draw Conclusions

You can **draw conclusions** about story characters and events by paying attention to facts you find in the selection.

Read the selection. Then answer each question to draw a conclusion.

Max lost his backpack. He looked on the floor, but all he saw were people's feet and the wheels of the shopping carts.

If my backpack is lost, so is my science report and my lucky baseball, Max thought.

Max searched for a lumpy, green backpack. Finally, he thought, Mom is going to buy a birthday cake. I better go tell her what happened.

Max let his nose lead him toward the bakery section. As the smell of pies and cookies became stronger, he saw her.

"Whew," he said to her. "It sure smells good around here." Then he spied something buried under all his mother's groceries. It was lumpy and green.

1. How do you think Max feels when he finds out he doesn't have his

    backpack? <u>He is probably worried because he looks for it, and so</u>

    <u>many things he needs are in it.</u>

2. What are some of Max's activities? <u>He plays baseball and has a</u>

    <u>science project.</u>

3. Why does Max go to find his mother in the bakery section? <u>She was</u>

    <u>going to buy a birthday cake.</u>

4. What does Max spy in his mother's shopping cart? <u>his backpack</u>

At Home: Ask students to draw some conclusions about what Max and his mother will do next.

Vocabulary

Identify the context clues in each sentence that could help you figure out the meaning of each underlined word. **Answers may vary.**

1. I couldn't eat the sauce because it had a sharp, bitter taste. **context**

   clues: eat, sharp, taste

2. Each crystal of sugar is as big as a tiny piece of salt or a grain of sand.

   context clues: sugar, tiny piece, grain

3. The boy gripped the handrail tightly as he slowly climbed the steep

   staircase. **context clues: handrail, tightly**

4. In Africa's animal kingdom, lions rule over many other animals of the

   region. **context clues: rule, the region**

5. One minute the bird was on the windowsill, and the next minute it was

   gone; it had simply vanished. **context clues: the next minute it was**

   gone

6. My head was dizzy from the whirling motion of the fairground ride.

   context clues: dizzy, motion

At Home: Have students define each of the vocabulary
194 words above in their own words.

Book 3.2/Unit 3
Two Bad Ants 6

The Hungry Dream

One night Jeremy dreamed of a faraway *kingdom*. The sky was yellow. The *whirling* red clouds were like spinning wheels. The grass was so tall, Jeremy *vanished* when he walked in it.

In the dream, Jeremy felt hungry. But he didn't see any food. He did see a path that led to a large shiny shape. When he got closer, he saw that it was a giant *crystal* with many points and sides. It had a door just big enough for Jeremy to enter.

Inside, people were eating. Jeremy ate the food, but it had a *bitter* taste. While he ate, the ground began to shake. Jeremy *gripped* the table.

Suddenly ... Jeremy woke up. The sky outside his window was blue!

1. Why was it that Jeremy *vanished* while walking in the far away *kingdom*?

   The grass in the kingdom was taller than he was.

2. What were the clouds in this *kingdom* doing?

   They were whirling through the sky.

3. How did the food Jeremy ate taste?

   bitter

4. What is another way to say "held tightly" in this story?

   gripped

5. Why does this *kingdom* appear and then disappear?

   It appears when Jeremy dreams, and disappears when he wakes up.

At Home: Have students draw and color an imaginary kingdom.

Story Comprehension

Review "Two Bad Ants." Then, in a few words or a sentence, describe the different parts of the story listed below.
Answers may vary.

1. First setting of story: <u>an ant hole</u>

2. Second setting of story: <u>a kitchen</u>

3. Main characters: <u>two ants</u>

4. Point of view: <u>the two ants</u>

5. Beginning of story: <u>A line of ants sets out to bring sugar crystals</u>
    <u>back for their queen.</u>

6. Middle of story: <u>The two bad ants stay behind in the kitchen</u>
    <u>and have several unpleasant adventures.</u>

7. End of story: <u>The two ants return home to their ant hole.</u>

8. Message of story: <u>We are happiest in our own homes with our</u>
    <u>own friends.</u>

At Home: Ask students to list the ways the ants described household items. Then ask them why the author didn't call these items by their familiar names.

195

Book 3.2/Unit 3
Two Bad Ants   8

McGraw-Hill School Division

Do an Author and Title Search

A card catalog can help you find a book by its title or by the author's name.

To use a card catalog on a computer, you need to type in a Keyword. This can be either the author's last name, a word from the title, or the subject. Try to choose a word that probably won't appear in a lot of other titles.

Read the problem stated below. Decide if it would be better to do an author or a title search. Write **Author** or **Title** in the space beside the problem. Then choose a Keyword you might use to find the book you want. **Answers may vary.**

	Author or Title	**Keyword**
1. You read a book by Dr. Seuss. Now you'd like to find other books he's written.	Author	Seuss
2. You read a book last year with the word *elephants* in the title. But you don't remember the whole name.	Title	elephants
3. You want to find out who wrote "The Wind in the Willows."	Title	Wind
4. Margaret Wise Brown is your favorite author. You want to see if she wrote any books of poetry.	Author	Brown
5. You're looking for a book about Greek myths written by Rosemary Wells.	Author	Wells

10 | Book 3.2/Unit 3
Two Bad Ants

At Home: Have students list two books they found by searching a library card catalog.

196

Draw Conclusions

A **conclusion** is what you decide to think about something after you have looked at the information. You can draw a conclusion about a story by considering the information the author gives you. You also can use what you know from your own experiences.

Draw your own conclusions about the two ants by answering each question. **Answers may vary.**

1. Do you think the ants enjoyed their day in the kitchen? <u>No.</u>

2. What information from the story helped you to draw your conclusion?

   They had many unpleasant surprises and were in dangerous

   situations. They were worn out by everything that happened.

3. Think about a challenging day you have had or a time when you had some unexpected surprises. How did you feel afterward? <u>**tired,**</u>

   unhappy

4. How do you think the ants felt after they returned home? <u>**happy,**</u>

   wiser, glad to be home

5. What information did you use to draw that conclusion? Think about information from the story and what you know from experience.

   The sounds coming from the ant hole seemed joyful to them. The

   two ants never felt happier. If I had experienced unpleasant

   surprises in a strange place, I would be happy to be home.

6. Do you think the two ants will ever stay behind again? Why or why not?

   No; they will be afraid that they might get into another dangerous

   situation.

At Home: Have students choose an event from the story, such as when the ants were in the cup of coffee and draw a conclusion about how the ants felt and why.

197

Book 3.2/Unit 3
Two Bad Ants

6

McGraw-Hill School Division

Author's Purpose, Point of View

Authors often have a **point of view,** or opinion about something, which they express through their writing.

Read the following passage. Then answer the questions about the author's purpose and point of view. **Answers may vary.**

> I hadn't been back to my hometown of Lakeside for thirty years. I expected to find some changes, but nothing had changed. I found out that an ice-cream cone still cost 25 cents. A sign at the Center Movie House said, "Come early to see the latest cartoon before the movie." And guess what? The movie cost 75 cents. But it wasn't the low prices that bothered me. It was the ghostly quiet and the deserted streets. I wondered what had happened.

1. Tell some things about the story that entertained you.

   Answers will vary. _____

   _____

2. What did the story inform you about the past?

   A cone used to cost 25 cents. A cartoon was shown before the

   movies. Movies cost 75 cents.

3. What is the author trying to persuade you to believe?   **The town of**

   Lakeside has been abandoned or has stood still in time.

4. What do you think is the author's attitude about Lakeside?

   The author has good memories about the town and wants to find

   out what has happened.

5. What do you think is the author's main purpose for writing the story?

   to entertain

5 | Book 3.2/Unit 3
Two Bad Ants

At Home: Ask students to explain their answer to
question 5.

198

Context Clues

To figure out the meaning of a new word, look at the words and sentences around it for clues.

Read each sentence and look at the underlined word. Circle the words or phrases that help you figure out the meaning of the underlined word. Then write the meaning on the line.

1. I hurt (one of the) fingers on my (hand,) so it was hard for me to write.

    one of the five parts at the end of a hand_____

2. I (knew) her name, (but) then I forgot it. I wish I could remember it.

    not to be able to remember_____

3. To make gray paint, (mix black paint with white) paint.

    a color made by mixing black and white_____

4. The chair was too hard for me, so I sat in a (softer) one.

    not soft_____

5. I (heard a cat) meowing softly.

    the sound that a cat makes_____

6. (May) is my favorite month of the year. My mother's favorite month is (March.)

    one of the twelve parts of a year_____

7. My shadow on the wall is much larger than I am. The (light) from the lamp (made everything look different)

    a dark spot when the light is blocked_____

8. He lost his burro in the thick jungle. The (little gray animal) could not be found.

    a small gray animal_____

At Home: Challenge students to write two sentences that include all of the underlined words above.

Book 3.2/Unit 3
Two Bad Ants

16

Make Inferences

Sometimes characters don't say exactly how they feel or what they are thinking. So readers must **infer** what the characters feel by what they say or how they act.

Read the descriptions in the left-hand column. Then, in the right-hand column, tell how you think each character feels. **Answers will vary.**

What the Character Says, Thinks, or Does	**How the Character Feels**
Before she went to bed, Ann made sure the kitten had food and water. She put out an extra bowl of water, just in case. Ann put down three more blankets in the box the kitten slept in.	1. Ann is a little worried about her kitten, or she feels like she has to take very good care of the kitten.
"I have never seen such a beautiful birthday cake," Grandfather said. "I can't believe you went to so much trouble just for me."	2. Grandfather feels very happy and thankful to be remembered on his birthday.
Jason and Steve both wanted to be Captain Hook in the school play. Jason got the part. Steve tried hard to put on a happy face before he met Jason after school.	3. Steve feels upset that he did not win the part but still likes Jason.
Rolf brought his two mice to class. When she saw the mice, Claire gripped the edge of her desk. She hoped she wouldn't burst into tears in front of the whole class.	4. Claire is afraid of mice and is also embarrassed that she is.

At Home: Have students show you the clues in the descriptions that helped them make their inferences.

Vocabulary

solve	crafty	communicate	brain	social	subject

1. Most apes are very _____**social**_____ and like to live together in large groups.

2. Some people _____**communicate**_____ with each other by using sign language.

3. Scientists don't know much about what goes on inside the _____**brain**_____ of an animal.

4. Animal behavior is one _____**subject**_____ that scientists like to study.

5. Mice are clever and can be _____**crafty**_____ when it comes to hiding and gathering food.

6. Many animals can _____**solve**_____ simple problems such as where to find food.

At Home: Ask students to make up one sentence that uses three of the vocabulary words on this page.

Book 3.2/Unit 3
Do Animals Think?

6

McGraw-Hill School Division

Jake the Brain

Jake is my cat. He is the smartest cat in the world. He is so smart that he can *solve* math problems. You might wonder how he learned about this *subject*. After all, Jake doesn't go to school. You might also wonder how Jake can *communicate* his answer.

First, you should know that Jake is a very *social* cat. He likes to work with people. Also, when it comes to math, Jake really uses his *brain*.

Sometimes I show Jake a piece of cat food. Next, I show him two more pieces. Then I ask him how many pieces there are. Jake puts his paw on one piece and meows. Then he puts his paw on the other two pieces and meows twice. I count the meows for the answer: three pieces of food! That is some *crafty* cat!

1. What school *subject* does Jake the cat know?

   math

2. What word in this story means "to pass along information"?

   communicate

3. What word describes the cat when he likes to work with others?

   social

4. What can Jake do with math problems?

   He can solve them.

5. How does Jake's owner feel about him?

   She or he is proud of him because he can solve math problems.

---

5 Book 3.2/Unit 3
Do Animals Think?

At Home: Have students make a crossword puzzle using the italicized words from the story.

201A

Story Comprehension

Think about "Do Animals Think?" Then complete the charts below.
Answers will vary.

Examples of Animals' Thinking	Animals' Instincts
1. Sheepdogs figure out a way to cut a sheep from the flock.	6. Sea otters use stones as hammers.
2. An octopus uses its arms to open a jar.	7. A salmon returns from the ocean to the same stream where it was hatched.
3. Wolves can make plans and change their behavior.	8. A honey bee does a dance that communicates.
4. A chimpanzee chooses the best stick or stone to crack a nut.	9. A beaver makes a dam out of mud, grasses, and sticks.
	10. A spider weaves a web.
5. A lion chases its prey toward another waiting lion.	11. Ants build and live in complicated colonies.
	12. A bird builds the right-sized nest.

At Home: Ask students to explain why a sea otter using a stone as a hammer to open a shell is different from a chimp choosing the best tool to crack a nut.

202

Book 3.2/Unit 3
Do Animals Think?
12

Use an Encyclopedia Index

Below you will see a sample page from an encyclopedia index. Use it to answers the questions that follow.

636   **Money**

Money M:649 *with pictures*
         Coins: Ci:439 *with pictures*
         Gold: G:234
         Shells (as money): S:324
Mongolia M:652 *with map*
Monkey (animal) **M:659** *with pictures and map*
         Spider S:543 *with picture*
Monster (legends)
         Dragon D:789
         Loch Ness L:238 *with picture*
         See also **Myths**
Montana M:713 *with pictures and maps*

1. What is the last entry word on this page? <u>Montana</u>

2. What is the guide word for this page? <u>Money</u>

3. In what volume and on what page would you find information on the

   state of Montana? <u>M:713</u>

4. In what volume and on what page would you find a picture of a spider

   monkey? <u>S:543</u>

5. In what volume and on what page would you find a map of Mongolia?

   <u>M:652</u>

5 | Book 3.2/Unit 3
Do Animals Think? | **At Home:** Ask students where they would look for a
map of Montana. | **203**

Make Inferences

When you read a nonfiction story, you can use the story's details to help you make **inferences**. The details can suggest the author's purpose for writing or the author's point of view about the subject.

Think about "Do Animals Think?" Read each question below. Write your inference. Then list one or two details in the story that help you explain your inference. **Answers will vary.**

1. What are the author's feelings about animals?

    Inference: <u>She is interested in them and likes them.</u>

    Details: <u>She says that salmon "are amazing," that "even a worm</u>

    <u>can learn to follow a maze!" and that a sheepdog "outsmarts" a</u>

    <u>sheep.</u>

2. Does the author think that scientists know everything about how animals "think"?

    Inference: <u>No; she thinks they have learned some things, but not</u>

    <u>everything.</u>

    Details: <u>Scientists are coming up with new ways to study animals'</u>

    <u>brain power. They often disagree. Some scientists think whales</u>

    <u>communicate; others do not.</u>

3. Does the author think that only human beings are smart?

    Inference: <u>No; she thinks that animals are smart, too.</u>

    Details: <u>Besides people, chimpanzees are the most famous</u>

    <u>tool-users. Chimps seem to think about the tools they use. Dogs</u>

    <u>that herd sheep probably think about what they are doing.</u>

At Home: Ask students to infer if a sheep is thinking when it tries not to leave the flock after a sheepdog has singled it out.

204

Book 3.2/Unit 3
Do Animals Think?

6

Form Generalizations

Some **generalizations** are comments, observations, or opinions that are based on a character's feelings or actions in a story.

Use the passage to answer the questions. **Answers will vary.**

> Carlos was telling his cousins about the time Aunt Marie went to work on a farm in California and ended up as an extra in a movie. Carlos loved telling the stories he had heard so often from his father. He thought they were exciting.
>
> "Who cares," Susan stopped him. "Let's go out and play baseball."
>
> That evening at dinner Carlos's father and uncle talked about their grandfather and how he first came to Texas from Mexico. When they spoke in Spanish, his cousins didn't even bother to listen. Carlos knew that none of the cousins spoke Spanish as well as their parents did, himself included. Still, he thought it was kind of cool to know two languages.

1. How do people feel when others ignore them? **They feel**

   embarrassed and hurt.

2. What can you learn by listening to older people? **You can learn about**

   the past and about history.

3. What does the story suggest about the difference between younger

   people and older people? **Younger people might not be so**

   interested in knowing about their past.

4. Why do you think that Carlos and his cousins don't speak Spanish as

   well as their parents do? **They probably speak English in school**

   and with their friends, and even at home most of the time.

At Home: Ask students to form a generalization about what people can learn by listening to family stories.

Multiple-Meaning Words

Words with more than one meaning are called **multiple-meaning words**. The words and sentences around a multiple-meaning word can help you define the word.

Read each sentence below. Use **context clues** in each sentence to define the meaning of each underlined word. Then match each multiple-meaning word with its definition. Write the letter of the definition on the line.

__h__ 1. It took us a <u>long</u> time to get home.

a. angry

__c__ 2. That hat is <u>mine</u>, not yours.

b. a tool to cut wood

__a__ 3. She was <u>cross</u> with me because I took her pencil without asking.

c. belonging to me

__i__ 4. I <u>saw</u> her new toy.

d. have in mind

__g__ 5. It was <u>mean</u> of you to make fun of him.

e. move from one side to the other

__j__ 6. The men worked in the coal <u>mine</u>.

f. to want very much

__f__ 7. I <u>long</u> to visit my grandmother in Florida.

g. not nice

__d__ 8. You don't understand what I <u>mean</u>.

h. not short

__b__ 9. I want a <u>saw</u> for my birthday.

i. looked at

__e__ 10. She let me <u>cross</u> the street

j. a large space under the ground

At Home: Have students check their answers in a dictionary.

Book 3.2/Unit 3
Do Animals Think? 10

Draw Conclusions

When you **draw conclusions**, you look for facts in the story to help you answer a question.

Read each set of facts and then read the conclusions. Which conclusion can you draw based on the facts? Write an **X** next to the correct conclusion.

FACTS	CONCLUSIONS
1. It takes 3 hours to wash two cars. Mary and Jo can work for 4 hours.	__X__ Mary and Jo can wash two cars. _____ Mary and Jo can only wash one car.
2. The rain filled the swimming pool all the way up to the top. Mr. Cray kept one eye on the clouds and one eye on the plug.	__X__ Mr. Cray may pull the plug if it keeps on raining. _____ Mr. Cray counted on the rain to fill the pool.
3. Ray promised to clean up his room after dinner. First though, he planned to watch a show about lions on TV.	_____ Ray enjoys cleaning his room. __X__ Ray may clean up his room after he watches a show.
4. The truck shook and shook. Tina was afraid that the oranges were about to roll off onto the bumpy dirt road.	__X__ Tina is driving on a bumpy dirt road. _____ Tina's truck is broken.
5. Anna's eyes filled with tears as she went up to accept her award and thank the audience.	_____ Anna is upset. __X__ Anna is very happy.

Vocabulary

Supply the vocabulary word that has almost the same meaning as the underlined words in each sentence.

considering conversation boasting hesitated interrupted seized

1. Dad <u>paused for a moment</u> before diving into the pool.

   hesitated_____

2. The mouse <u>grabbed</u> the piece of cheese. _____ **seized** _____

3. Julie always <u>broke in</u> while her mother was speaking.

   interrupted_____

4. René was <u>bragging</u> about the size of his boat. _____ **boasting** _____

5. <u>Keeping in mind</u> that she hadn't rehearsed, Sarah played her part well.

   considering_____

6. My brother and I had a friendly <u>talk</u>.

   conversation_____

At Home: Have students make up three sentences, each using two of the vocabulary words.

Book 3.2/Unit 3
"Wilbur's Boast"
from Charlotte's Web

6

The Buzz About Flies

When the teacher asked Andrew to work with Cicely on a science project, both students looked unhappy. They had never even had a *conversation* before. They didn't know each other.

Cicely *hesitated* to tell Andrew about her project idea. When she began to speak about it, she was *interrupted* by a loud buzz.

Andrew reached up and *seized* a fly. As he was *boasting* about how he had caught the fly, it flew out of his hand.

"I'll get it," Cicely said. She followed the fly quietly.

When it landed on a wall, she cupped her hand around it. "I've got it!" she said. "And I've got an idea for our project!"

Considering what had just happened, Andrew was not surprised to hear Cicely's idea. "We should do our project on flies," she suggested.

1. What had Andrew and Cicely never had with each other?

    a conversation

2. What was it that Cicely *hesitated* to do?

    tell Andrew her project idea

3. How was Cicely *interrupted*?

    A fly buzzed over her head.

4. What did Andrew do when the fly was buzzing?

    He seized it.

5. How did the fly end up being helpful to Cicely and Andrew?

    It gave them an idea for their science project.

5

Book 3.2/Unit 3
"Wilbur's Boast"
from Charlotte's Web

At Home: Encourage students to make a small science project by drawing and labeling an insect or animal they would like to know more about.

208A

Story Comprehension

Think about "Wilbur's Boast." Then write a sentence or sentences to fill in the chart. **Answers may vary.**

1. **SETTING:**

   The story takes place in a barn on a farm._____

2. **HOW DOES THE SETTING AFFECT THE PLOT?**

   The characters all live on the farm and that is where the_____

   action takes place._____

3. **MAIN CHARACTERS:**

   The main characters are Charlotte, a spider; Wilbur, a pig;____

   Fern, a girl; and Templeton, a rat._____

4. **DESCRIBE EACH MAIN CHARACTER:**

   Wilbur is curious and boastful and tries to do things he_____

   cannot do. Charlotte is wise, kind, and fun-loving. Fern is____

   kind and loves Wilbur. Templeton is helpful._____

5. **PLOT:**

   Wilbur tries to spin a web, but he fails twice._____

Do an Electronic Subject Search

An electronic subject search on a library computer will tell you what books will give you information. Pretend you typed in the subject "Farming Today." Here is what the computer's first screen shows.

```
F arming T oday
```

```
1. Life on a F arm         Nicole Erwin  ©1998  Click Here for Full Record
2. F arm Equipment Repairs Bruce Quilby  ©1995  Click Here for Full Record
3. Backwoods V ermont      Tanya Pullan  ©1994  Click Here for Full Record
4. The Last F amily F arm  Barry Langlen ©1988  Click Here for Full Record

38 books found      (B) = go back        (R) = go to next screen
```

Answer the following questions by using the results of the computer catalog search.

1. Which book was published most recently? _____ **Life on a Farm** _____

2. Which book would tell you how to repair a tractor? **Farm Equipment**

   Repairs _____

3. How many different books did the computer find? _____ **38** _____

4. Which book contains information about just one state?

   Backwoods Vermont _____

5. How would you see more of this list? _____ **Select (R) to see the next**

   screen. _____

5 Book 3.2/Unit 3
   "Wilbur's Boast"
   from Charlotte's Web

At Home: Ask students to list three subjects they would like to investigate in a subject search by computer.

210

Draw Conclusions

Readers can **draw conclusions** about a character or a story event based on the information and facts they find in the story.

Answer each question by using information in "Wilbur's Boast" to draw a conclusion.

1. Why does Wilbur look around to see if a piece of rope was following him the first time he falls? **Charlotte told him to let down a dragline as he went down, and he didn't really know what it meant. He just thought whatever it was would be there.**

2. How does Charlotte feel when Wilbur falls the first time? **She is amused; she is laughing.**

3. Why does Wilbur climb to the top of the pile and try to spin a web again? **because he is not a quitter**

4. How do Charlotte and Fern feel about Wilbur? **They are truly fond of him.**

5. How does Wilbur feel about falling when he tried to spin a web? **He thinks it serves him right because he was trying to show off.**

6. Why does Charlotte tell the story about the bridge? **She wants to prove that people aren't as good at spinning webs as spiders are.**

McGraw-Hill School Division

Form Generalizations

Read each generalization about fairy tales. Tell whether you think the generalization is true or false. Then explain your answer. You may want to use the name of a fairy tale as an example.
Answers may vary.

1. Fairy tales are make-believe. **True; fairy tales do not talk about real people or events.**

2. Some fairy tales have characters who are mean people.
   True; Cinderella has wicked stepsisters and a wicked stepmother.

3. Fairy tales are too scary for little children to hear or watch. **False; some children may not be scared by them.**

4. Many fairy tales begin by saying, "Once upon a time..." **True; many fairy tales start this way.**

5. Everyone loves fairy tales. **False; some people do, and some people do not.**

5 | Book 3.2/Unit 3
"Wilbur's Boast"
from Charlotte's Web

At Home: Ask students to make a generalization about fairy tales.

212

Context Clues

If you see an unfamiliar word, try looking at the words and phrases around it for **context clues**.

Read each sentence and look at the underlined word. Write the correct meaning for the word. Then write a new sentence that includes the underlined word. **Answers will vary.**

1. My mother has a <u>different</u> last name than I do. Her last name is Moser, and my last name is Brown.

   Meaning: <u>not the same</u>

   Sentence: <u>Possible answer: Those two girls are very</u>

   <u>different from each other.</u>

2. Today, we <u>discussed</u> pollution. People talked a lot about it.

   Meaning: <u>talked about</u>

   Sentence: <u>Possible answer: Yesterday I discussed the news with</u>

   <u>my father.</u>

3. I saw some men fishing down by the lake. The <u>fishermen</u> asked me if I wanted to learn how to fish.

   Meaning: <u>men who fish</u>

   Sentence: <u>Possible answer: Fishermen catch many different fish.</u>

4. If you throw a ball in water, it will not sink. It will <u>float</u> on top.

   Meaning: <u>to stay on top of the water</u>

   Sentence: <u>Possible answer: He learned how to float on his back.</u>

At Home: Have students circle the context clues in the examples.

Book 3.2/Unit 3
"Wilbur's Boast"
from Charlotte's Web

8

McGraw-Hill School Division

Author's Purpose, Point of View

Authors write for different **purposes**. They may write to inform, to entertain, or to persuade. For example, the purpose of a report may be to inform; the purpose of a fiction story may be to entertain; and the purpose of a letter or an advertisement may be to persuade.

Think of a subject to write about for each purpose listed below. Then write a sentence about each subject. **Answers will vary.**

Inform

1. Subject:

   _____

2. About subject:

   _____

   _____

Entertain

3. Subject:

   _____

4. About subject:

   _____

   _____

Persuade

5. Subject:

   _____

6. About subject:

   _____

   _____

6 Book 3.2/Unit 3
The Koala Catchers   **At Home:** Encourage students to include a small
drawing with each of their subject choices.   **214**

Vocabulary

Fill in the blanks with the correct word. Both blank lines for each number should be filled in with the same word.

| rescuers | loops | snug | starve | strip | crates |

1. We packed the oranges in large _____crates_____ to ship them overseas. _____Crates_____ keep things in place while they travel over a long distance.

2. The bear cubs were warm and _____snug_____ in their cave throughout the winter. We were safe and _____snug_____ in our house!

3. The trainer gently _____loops_____ the rope around the horse's neck. Then she _____loops_____ the other end of the rope around a fence post and ties it tightly.

4. Thanks to the _____rescuers_____ we were all saved from the freezing cold. It took the _____rescuers_____ four hours to find us.

5. During the winter, many animals _____strip_____ bark from the trees for food. They _____strip_____ moss from rocks and eat that as well.

6. Bears eat plenty of food during the fall, so they don't _____starve_____ during the cold and snowy winter. We store lots of food in the kitchen, so we don't _____starve_____ either!

At Home: Have students choose one of the vocabulary words and make up two related sentences, each of which includes the word.

Book 3.2/Unit 3
The Koala Catchers 6

McGraw-Hill School Division

A Trip to Remember

One day while camping, I heard a noise in the woods. My family walked toward the noise. We found a baby bear with its leg caught in the *loops* of a rope.

The rope was tied around a tree. When the bear pulled at the rope, it would *strip* off the bark of the tree.

My mother and I waited near the baby bear while my father went to the park ranger's cabin. This bear needed some trained *rescuers*.

When the ranger came she had two *crates*: a large one and a small one. The bear fit in the small one. Now it was safe and *snug*.

"I will feed the bear right away so it will not *starve*," said the ranger. "Then we'll find the bear's home."

That was one camping trip I will always remember!

1. What was the bear caught in?

   <u>the loops of a rope</u>

2. What did the bear *strip* off the tree?

   <u>bark</u>

3. Who did the father go to look for at the park ranger's cabin?

   <u>bear rescuers</u>

4. What made the baby bear safe and *snug*?

   <u>the small crate</u>

5. Why does the speaker say that was a trip always to be remembered?

   <u>Because the child and his parents helped rescue a baby bear.</u>

At Home: Invite students to write a short story about rescuing an animal in danger.

215A

Story Comprehension

Suppose you are writing a summary of "The Koala Catchers." Review the information in the selection. Then write answers to the following questions. **Answers may vary.**

Where does the story take place?

1. **Kangaroo Island, Australia,** _____

When does the story take place?

2. **present time** _____

What do the rescuers do?

3. **They catch the koalas, put them in crates, and fly them to another**

   place. _____

4. **They plant new trees that the koalas like to eat.** _____

Why do the rescuers plant new trees?

5. **Koalas only eat the leaves of eucalyptus trees.** _____

6. **There are so many koalas that they strip the leaves of the trees on**

   Kangaroo Island, and there isn't enough for them all to eat. _____

What are koalas like?

7. **They are wild animals with claws that live in trees and eat the**

   leaves of trees. _____

8. **Babies stay in their mother's pouches for 6 months and then ride**

   on their mother's backs for 6 months. _____

At Home: Ask students to tell you how the fact that koalas only eat eucalyptus leaves causes problems for them.

216

Book 3.2/Unit 3
The Koala Catchers

8

McGraw-Hill School Division

Use a Resource

When you're doing a student project, you might choose to use one or more of these resources for information.

newspaper   encyclopedia   dictionary

card catalog   telephone book

Which resources would you use to complete each project below? Write their names and the information you could find in each one. **Possible answers are shown.**

1. You want to find words in American English that come from French and Spanish. <u>**dictionary for word origins; card catalog for a book**</u>

   <u>**on languages; encyclopedia for France and Spain (food words**</u>

   <u>**and geographical features, etc.)**</u>

2. You need to gather your classmates to put on a play. <u>**telephone**</u>

   <u>**book for their phone numbers**</u>

3. You need to write a report about a local election for mayor.

   <u>**newspaper for local events; telephone book for candidates' phone**</u>

   <u>**numbers**</u>

4. You need to draw a map of Canada. <u>**encyclopedia for a map;**</u>

   <u>**card catalog to find a book on Canada**</u>

5. You want to find out about the weather in the Philippine Islands.

   <u>**newspaper for weather reports; encyclopedia for the country's**</u>

   <u>**weather; card catalog for a book about life in the Philippines**</u>

Form Generalizations

A **generalization** is a broad statement that is based on examples.

Read the following generalizations that were made based on "The Koala Catchers." Write two examples or facts from the selection that support each generalization. **Answers may vary.**

Generalization: Koala bears are difficult to capture.

1. <u>They live in the tops of trees.</u>

2. <u>Koalas are wild animals.</u>

Generalization: Some people try to rescue koala bears.

3. <u>Koala Rescue has moved 650 koalas to new homes.</u>

4. <u>In the 1920s people moved koalas to Kangaroo Island where</u>
   <u>they had a lot to eat.</u>

Generalization: You will never find a koala bear living on the ground.

5. <u>The koala eats leaves high in the tree tops.</u>

6. <u>They come down from the trees only to move to another tree.</u>

Generalization: Baby koalas stay close to their mothers.

7. <u>Baby koalas stay in their mothers' pouches for six months.</u>

8. <u>Baby koalas ride on their mothers' backs for six months.</u>

At Home: Ask students to make a generalization about the importance of rescuing koala bears based on the information in "The Koala Catchers."

Context Clues

When you find an unfamiliar word, read the words and sentences around it. They often can help you figure out the word's meaning.

Look at the word in dark type in each sentence. Underline the clues that help you figure out the word's meaning. Then mark an **X** next to the meaning of the word in dark type.

1. We flew to Mexico on an **airplane**. It took much less time than a train would have.

    __X__ **a.** a flying machine   _____ **b.** a bell

    _____ **c.** a person who acts   _____ **d.** a helper

2. It's hard to **decide** what to do. I just can't make up my mind.

    _____ **a.** to pay someone   _____ **b.** to take

    _____ **c.** to refuse   __X__ **d.** to make up one's mind

3. My mother said, "It's six o'clock—almost **dinnertime**. We're having chicken."

    _____ **a.** part of a person's face   _____ **b.** a large balloon

    __X__ **c.** a time when people eat dinner   _____ **d.** a dinner plate

4. We heard a loud **crash**. A tree had fallen outside.

    _____ **a.** a break   _____ **b.** a small bow

    _____ **c.** a small water animal   __X__ **d.** a loud noise

5. I call my **dentist** when my tooth hurts.

    _____ **a.** someone who cuts wood   __X__ **b.** someone who fixes teeth

    _____ **c.** someone who bakes bread   _____ **d.** someone who cuts hair

Multiple-Meaning Words

When you come across a **multiple-meaning word**, use the words and sentences around it to understand its meaning.

The words in dark type below have more than one meaning. Use **context clues** to help you choose a word or phrase from the box that means the same as the word in dark type. Then write the word or phrase on the line after each sentence.

look at	something that can be heard
a line of railroad cars	make a picture of something
choose	a piece of metal that fits in a lock
cause	a small river

1. I used my **key** to open the door. <u>a piece of metal that fits in a lock</u>

2. Did you hear that loud **sound**? <u>something that can be heard</u>

3. I like to **draw** my cat. <u>make a picture of something</u>

4. Did you **see** the beautiful paintings? <u>look at</u>

5. We took the **train** to Florida. <u>a line of railroad cars</u>

6. He will **pick out** a new game at the store. <u>choose</u>

7. She will **make** her bicycle move more slowly. <u>cause</u>

8. The **stream** was shallow; it hadn't rained in a long time. <u>a small river</u>

At Home: Have students write sentences using the other meaning of each multiple-meaning word.

Unit 3 Vocabulary Review

A. Supply the correct word from the box.

---

mistakes   perform   talented   brain   subject   conversation   boasting

---

One day Brian and Jill had a ____conversation____ . This is what they said.

Brian: Sam is always ____boasting____ .

Jill: Yes, I know. He says he has the best ____brain____ in the class.

Brian: But he's not good in every ____subject____ . I'm better in science.

Jill: Yes. He makes ____mistakes____ like the rest of us.

Brian: Even if he is ____talented____ , he doesn't have to ____perform____ all the time.

B. Put an **X** next to the word you could use in place of the underlined vocabulary word.

1. It felt <u>snug</u> under the covers.

   a. safe _____   **b.** warm _____   **c.** cozy __X__

2. A fast twist sent the top <u>whirling</u>.

   a. running _____   **b.** spinning __X__   **c.** flying _____

3. Heather <u>seized</u> the dog's ball and threw it again.

   a. grabbed __X__   **b.** tossed _____   **c.** bounced _____

McGraw-Hill School Division

At Home: Have students write a conversation like the one in Part A. They should use at least four vocabulary words in their conversation.

Unit 3 Vocabulary Review

A. Supply the correct word from the box.

| equipment | bitter | invisible | considering | crates | communicate |

1. The juice tasted _____**bitter**_____ to Nobu.

2. Ms. Warner packed her dishes in _____**crates**_____ .

3. People can talk and _____**communicate**_____ by using their hands.

4. She was _____**considering**_____ which book to buy.

5. You need lots of _____**equipment**_____ to play hockey.

6. Katy pretended to have an _____**invisible**_____ dog.

B. Read each definition. Choose a word from the box and write it on the line.

| social | rescuers | hesitated | boasting |

1. animals that live in groups _____**social**_____

2. waited before you acted _____**hesitated**_____

3. people who save animals _____**rescuers**_____

4. telling how great you are _____**boasting**_____

At Home: Have students write a sentence for each
vocabulary word in Part B.

Book 3.2/Unit 3
Unit 3 Vocabulary Review 10

McGraw-Hill School Division